DISCOVERY

Early History of Israel
Exodus – Joshua

STUDENT WORKBOOK

AUTHOR
PATRICIA C. RUSSELL

EDITORS
MRS. NELLIE E. CONSTANCE
MRS. LOIS EADES, M.A.

COVER ART & GRAPHIC DESIGN
TROY D. RUSSELL

PROJECT EDITOR
TOM M. CONSTANCE JR.

EXPLORER'S BIBLE STUDY
P.O. BOX 425
DICKSON, TN 37056-0425

ISBN 978-1-889015-33-0

Printed 2009

*We believe the Bible is God's Word, a divine revelation, in the original language
verbally inspired in its entirety, and that it is the supreme infallible authority
in all matters of faith and conduct.*
(2 Peter 1:21; 2 Timothy 3:16)

Printed in the United States of America

Published by Explorer's Bible Study
2652 Hwy. 46 South
P.O. Box 425
Dickson, TN 37056-0425

615-446-7316
www.explorerbiblestudy.org

Contents

About the Author

Patricia Russell has been a Christian educator for over 25 years. She began her teaching career by establishing a home preschool. Later she accepted a position as a teacher in a private Christian school and also served as a curriculum coordinator and consultant. Most recently, she helped to cofound Carden Christian Academy, a non-denominational school serving students preschool – 8th grade. Through years of writing and development, she has crafted a curriculum that comes from practical "hands on" experience. This curriculum has been "classroom tested" in Christian schools, in home school settings, as well as having been used in Explorer's Bible Study classes throughout the U.S.

Patricia's goal in developing this curriculum is to provide the young Bible scholar with a chronological and historical method of Bible study. It is through this means that the Bible is studied in its entirety, rather than fragmented. The importance of understanding the true meaning of God's Word and His plan for each of us comes through careful study. Interpretation follows a knowledge of what God says, what God means, and finally how each individual applies this knowledge to his or her personal life experience.

A Note to Parents and Teachers

If you have said "yes" to the call of God to teach, you have accepted one of the most important challenges in building the future kingdom. In James 3:1 we read "Let not many of you become teachers, knowing that we shall receive a stricter judgment." It takes a great commitment to put yourself in a place of responsibility in which children and young students will make life-changing decisions. Knowing the high expectations God has for those who commit to this calling should not deter you from this wonderful and powerful opportunity to serve in this way. As you see the loving response to God from a child or student, it is difficult—if not impossible—to imagine NOT teaching! It becomes a compelling urgency that God rewards in so many ways that you'll wonder why there was ever a question mark after the words, "Should I consider teaching?"

Whether you are a home schooling parent, a Sunday School teacher, or a Christian educator, God has chosen you to teach! As a teacher, you will have a great influence in the lives of your children or students. You have been given the responsibility by God to mentor these lives spiritually. It is an awesome responsibility, but you don't have to do it alone! God is with you every step of the way.

Teach each child faithfully, prayerfully, and consistently in His Word—knowing it, believing it, living it, and then teaching it. Teaching is impossible without the first three. We hope this Bible curriculum will help guide you through this process.

A Teacher must have:

1. a personal commitment to Christ.

2. a love for students with a desire to guide them in understanding God's Word.

3. a call to the ministry through God's Word.

4. a personal commitment to daily Bible study.

"And these words which I command you today shall be in your heart. You shall teach them diligently to your children, and shall talk of them when you sit in your house, when you walk by the way, when you lie down, and when you rise up."
Deuteronomy 6:6-7

Plan of Study for the Student

The lessons in this workbook will help you learn more about God and to understand His Word—the Bible.

As you study. . .

Pray that God will give you understanding.
Discover what the BIBLE says.
Choose to live God's way every day.
Never stop learning and growing. . .
There is always MORE!

The lessons are divided into five days of questions, plus a lesson review.

1. READ the Scripture Text Box or Bible passage given.
2. Check the Word/Phrase Meanings found in the text.
3. Answer each question, following the text. As you do this, you will discover that as you read and write God's Word you will understand what it means. The questions ask *Who, What, When, Where, Why,* or *How.* The purpose is to help you comprehend and develop a pattern of organized thinking.
4. Complete the Map Studies so you can visualize where Bible events took place.
5. Do the Lesson Review to see how much you learned!

Bible Journal and Memory

We suggest that you get a spiral notebook or 3 ring binder and keep a Bible Journal of your study of Early History of Israel. You will find this elephant symbol throughout your lessons. Your memory verses for the week will be in **bold type**. Write these verses in  your Bible Journal and do your best to memorize as many verses as you can each week. Writing the verses will make it easier for you to memorize. You may also want to use your Bible Journal to write down important things that you have learned as you study your lesson. . . or use a page to illustrate a story from a lesson. Be CREATIVE!

Your word I have hidden in my heart, that I might not sin against You.
Psalm 119:11

Take the Extra Challenge!

1. Read the entire text in your Bible or listen with Bible CD's if you have these available to you.
2. Choose five words that are new to you from the word box and write a sentence for each.
3. Write a short essay telling what you learned about God from the lesson.
4. Do a short news release about a Bible character or event in the lesson.
5. Research a place on the map study and write a short report on current events there.

DISCOVERY

THE ISRAELITES IN BONDAGE

DAY ONE
EXODUS 1:7-11

7 But the children of Israel were fruitful and increased abundantly, multiplied and *grew exceedingly mighty*; and the land was filled with them.

8 Now there arose a new king over Egypt, who did not know Joseph.

9 And he said to his people, "Look, the people of the children of Israel are more and **mightier** than we;

10 "come, let us deal **shrewdly** with them, lest they multiply, and it happen, **in the event** of war, that they also join our enemies and fight against us, and so go up out of the land."

11 Therefore they set **taskmasters** over them to **afflict** them with their **burdens**. And they built for Pharaoh **supply cities**, Pithom and Raamses.

Word Meanings:
1. **mightier:** stronger
2. **shrewdly:** wisely deceptive
3. **taskmasters:** ones who demand work
4. **afflict:** torment, make to suffer
5. **burdens:** heavy loads of work
6. **observe:** notice by watching
7. **required:** demanded

Phrase Meanings:
1. **grew exceedingly mighty:** became very numerous
2. **in the event:** in case this happens
3. **supply cities:** providing what is needed from certain cities
4. **dealt with:** how someone is treated

Questions:

1. What happened in Egypt? _____

2. Whom did the new king not know? _____

3. What two things did the king want his people to **observe** about the children of Israel?

    a) _____

    b) _____

4. How did he say they should be **dealt with**? _____

5. Why did he say that this would be necessary? _____

6. What two things did he think would happen in the event of a war?

    a) _____

    b) _____

7.   What did the Egyptians set over the Israelites? _____

8.   What was the reason for this? _____

9.   What were the Israelites **required** to do? _____

10. What were the names of these cities?

     a) _____

     b) _____

DAY TWO
EXODUS 1:12-16

12 But the more they afflicted them, the more they multiplied and grew. And they were **in dread** of the children of Israel.

13 So the Egyptians made the children of Israel serve with **rigor**.

14 And they made their lives **bitter** with hard **bondage**—in **mortar**, in brick, and in **all manner of service** in the field. All their service in which they made them serve was with rigor.

15 Then the king of Egypt spoke to the Hebrew **midwives**, of whom the name of one was Shiphrah and the name of the other Puah;

16 and he said, "When you do the duties of a midwife for the Hebrew women, and see them on the birthstools, if it is a son, then you shall kill him; but if it is a daughter, then she shall live."

Word Meanings:
1. **rigor:** severe hardship
2. **bitter:** harsh
3. **bondage:** slavery
4. **mortar:** mixture used to join bricks and stones
5. **midwives:** women who help in the birth of a baby
6. **occurred:** happened
7. **emotion:** a strong feeling
8. **accomplish:** bring to a successful conclusion

Phrase Meanings:
1. **in dread:** terrible fear
2. **all manner of service:** the way in which the work was done

Questions:

1.   What **occurred** when the Egyptians afflicted the Israelites? _____

     _____

2.   What **emotion** did the Egyptians have? _____

3.   Because of this, what did they do to the children of Israel?

     a) _____

     b) _____

4.   How did they **accomplish** this? _____

5.   What two materials are mentioned that the Israelites needed for their work?

        a) _____

        b) _____

6.   What else was made difficult? _____

7.   What instruction did Pharaoh give the Hebrew midwives? _____

    _____

8.   What were the names of the midwives? _____

9.   When did Pharaoh tell them to carry out his instruction? _____

    _____

10. What were they to do about the girls who were born? _____

DAY THREE
EXODUS 1:17-22

17 But the midwives **feared God**, and did not do as the king of Egypt commanded them, but saved the male children alive.

18 So the king of Egypt called for the midwives and said to them, "Why have you done this thing, and saved the male children alive?"

19 And the midwives said to Pharaoh, "Because the Hebrew women are not like the Egyptian women; for they are lively and give birth before the midwives come to them."

20 Therefore God dealt well with the midwives, and the people multiplied and grew very mighty.

21 And so it was, because the midwives feared God, that He **provided households** for them.

22 So Pharaoh commanded all his people, saying, "Every son who is born you shall cast into the river, and every daughter you shall save alive."

Word Meanings:
1. **respond:** answer

2. **compare:** show difference

Phrase Meanings:
1. **feared God:** respected and honored God

2. **provided households:** gave them a house for their family

Questions:

1. Whom did the midwives fear? _____

2. What did the midwives do? _____

3. Whom were they disobeying? _____

4. What did Pharaoh, the king of Egypt, do? _____

5. What did the king say to them? _____
   _____

6. How did the midwives **respond**? _____
   _____

7. With whom did they **compare** the Hebrew women? _____

8. What did God do? _____

9. What was the result?

   a) _____

   b) _____

10. What else did God do for the midwives because they feared Him? _____
    _____

11. What did Pharaoh command all his people to do?

    a) _____

    b) _____

DAY FOUR
EXODUS 2:1-6

1 And a man of the house of Levi went and took as wife a daughter of Levi.

2 So the woman **conceived** and **bore** a son. And when she saw that he was a beautiful child, she hid him three months.

3 But when she could no longer hide him, she took an **ark of bulrushes** for him, **daubed** it with **asphalt** and **pitch**, put the child in it, and laid it in the **reeds** by the river's bank.

4 And his sister stood **afar** off, to know what would be done to him.

5 Then the daughter of Pharaoh came down to bathe at the river. And her maidens walked along the riverside; and when she saw the ark among the reeds, she sent her maid to get it.

6 And when she had opened it, she saw the child, and behold, the baby wept. So she had **compassion** on him, and said, "This is one of the Hebrews' children."

Word Meanings:

1. **conceived:** to become pregnant with a child
2. **bore:** given birth to
3. **daubed:** to smear over the surface of an object
4. **asphalt:** a sticky substance mixed with gravel
5. **pitch:** a thick dark mixture used to keep water out
6. **reeds:** long leaves of a plant which grows by the water
7. **afar:** a distance away
8. **compassion:** feeling of tenderness
9. **constructed:** made

Phrase Meaning:

ark of bulrushes: waterproof basket made with the leaves of a plant

Questions:

1. What did the Levite woman do when she gave birth to a son? _____

   _____

2. What did she do when she could no longer do this? _____

   _____

3. With what materials was it **constructed**? _____

4. What did she do when the ark was finished? _____

   _____

5. Where did she put the ark? _____

   _____

6. Who was standing afar off? _____

7. Why was she watching? _____

8. Who came to bathe at the river? _____

9. Where were they walking? _____

10. What did Pharaoh's daughter see? _____

11. What did she do when she saw it? _____

12. What happened when she opened the ark? _____

13. What did the baby do? _____

14. What did Pharaoh's daughter feel for the baby? _____

15. What did she say about the baby? _____

    _____

DAY FIVE

EXODUS 2:7-10

7 Then his sister said to Pharaoh's daughter, "Shall I go and call a nurse for you from the Hebrew women, that she may **nurse** the child for you?"

8 And Pharaoh's daughter said to her, "Go." So the maiden went and called the child's mother.

9 Then Pharaoh's daughter said to her, "Take this child away and nurse him for me, and I will give you your **wages**." So the woman took the child and nursed him.

10 And the child grew, and she brought him to Pharaoh's daughter, and he became her son. So she called his name *Moses*, saying, "Because I drew him out of the water."

Word Meanings:
1. **nurse:** to feed a baby milk from the breast
2. **wages:** payment for services

Name Meaning:
Moses: to draw out (of the water)

Questions:

1. What question did the sister ask Pharaoh's daughter?_____

    _____

2. From where would the sister get a nurse? _____

3. What did Pharaoh's daughter tell her to do? _____

4. Whom did the maiden call? _____

5. What did Pharaoh's daughter tell the mother to do?

    a) _____

    b) _____

6. What would Pharaoh's daughter give the mother? _____

7. What did the woman do? _____

8. What happened after the child grew?

    a) _____

    b) _____

9. What did she call his name? _____

10. What reason did she give for this name? _____

    _____

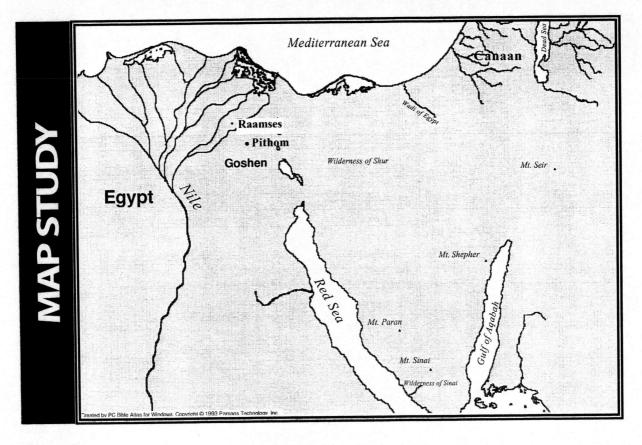

Questions:

1. Identify the following: (highlight or circle)

   a) Egypt   d) Raamses

   b) Goshen   e) Canaan

   c) Pithom

2. Use a blue highlighter (or pencil) to color and trace the Nile River.

3. Draw a line from Canaan to Egypt showing where the Israelites came during the famine when Joseph was a ruler in Egypt (from Genesis study).

4. Color the area of Goshen with a green colored pencil showing where the Israelites lived for four hundred and thirty years.

5. Put an X by the supply cities that the Israelites built for Pharaoh.

REVIEW
LESSON ONE   Exodus 1:7 - 2:10

A. Write the correct letter(s) in the blank.

_____ 1. Whom did the new king (Pharaoh) forget?
      a) Jacob
      b) Abraham
      c) Joseph

_____ 2. The Egyptians made slaves of the Hebrews because
      a) they were good farmers.
      b) they were more and mightier.
      c) Pharaoh respected their work.

_____ 3. The Hebrew midwives kept the baby boys alive because
      a) they did not like Pharaoh.
      b) they were friends of the Israelites.
      c) they feared God.

_____ 4. Which of the following cities did the Israelites build for Pharaoh?
      a) Raamses
      b) Etham
      c) Pithom

_____ 5. To whom did Pharaoh give the following command: "Every son who is born you shall cast into the river"?
      a) the midwives
      b) his officers
      c) the taskmasters
      d) all his people

B. Who said the following?

_____ 1. "Why have you saved the male children?"

_____ 2. "Because I drew him out of the water."

_____ 3. "The Hebrew women are not like the Egyptian women."

_____ 4. "Shall I go and call a nurse?"

_____ 5. "Look, the people are more and mightier than we."

a) Pharaoh's daughter   b) midwives   c) Pharaoh   d) sister of the baby

8

 # DISCOVERY

GOD REMEMBERS HIS PEOPLE

DAY ONE
EXODUS 2:11-14

> **11 Now it came to pass** in those days, when Moses was grown, that he went out to his brethren and looked at their burdens. And he saw an Egyptian beating a Hebrew, one of his brethren.
>
> **12** So he looked this way and that way, and when he saw no one, he killed the Egyptian and hid him in the sand.
>
> **13** And when he went out the second day, behold, two Hebrew men were fighting, and he said to the one who did the wrong, "Why are you striking your companion?"
>
> **14** Then he said, "Who made you a prince and a judge over us? Do you intend to kill me as you killed the Egyptian?" So Moses feared and said, "Surely this thing is known!"

Word Meanings:
1. **relationship:** a relative; related by blood or marriage
2. **precautions:** careful actions taken before something is **done**

Phrase Meaning:
Now it came to pass: It happened like this....

Questions:

1. Where did Moses go when he was grown? _____
   _____

2. What did he do? _____

3. What did he see?_____

4. What was the **relationship** between Moses and the man?_____
   _____

5. What words tell us that Moses took **precautions** before he took action on what he saw?
   _____

6. Did he notice that anyone could see him? _____

7. What two things did Moses do?

   a) _____

   b) _____

8.   What happened when Moses went out the second day? _____

_____

9.   What question did Moses ask? _____

_____

10. To whom was the question asked? _____

11. With what two questions did the man respond?

a) _____

b) _____

12. Why was Moses fearful? _____

_____

DAY TWO
EXODUS 2:15-20

15 When Pharaoh heard of this matter, he **sought** to kill Moses. But Moses **fled** from the face of Pharaoh and dwelt in the land of Midian; and he sat down by a well.

16 Now the priest of Midian had seven daughters. And they came and drew water, and they filled the **troughs** to water their father's flock.

17 Then the shepherds came and drove them away; but Moses stood up and helped them, and watered their flock.

18 When they came to Reuel their father, he said, "How is it that you have come so soon today?"

19 And they said, "An Egyptian delivered us from the hand of the shepherds, and he also drew enough water for us and watered the flock."

20 So he said to his daughters, "And where is he? Why is it that you have left the man? Call him, that he **may eat bread**."

Word Meanings:
1. **sought:** searched for
2. **fled:** ran away; escaped
3. **troughs:** long containers where animals get water
4. **imply:** suggest; mean to say

Phrase Meaning:
may eat bread: to invite one to have a meal

Questions:

1.   What did Pharaoh do when he heard what Moses had done? _____

_____

2.   Where had Moses gone? _____

3.   What did Moses do? _____

4.   How many daughters did the priest of Midian have? _____

5.   Why had they come to the well where Moses was? _____

6.   What did they do? _____

7.   Why did they do this? _____

8.   Who then came to the well? _____

9.   What did they do? _____

10. What two things did Moses do?

      a) _____

      b) _____

11. What question did Reuel, their father ask? _____

_____

12. What did this question **imply**? _____

_____

13. What did the daughters respond to their father?

      a) _____

_____

      b) _____

_____

14. What two questions did the father then ask?

      a) _____

      b) _____

15. What did he tell them to do? _____

_____

DAY THREE
EXODUS 2:21-25

21 Then Moses was **content** to live with the man, and he gave Zipporah his daughter to Moses.

22 And she bore him a son, and he called his name **Gershom**; for he said, "I have been a stranger in a **foreign** land."

23 Now it happened **in the process of time** that the king of Egypt died. Then the children of Israel **groaned** because of the bondage, and they cried out; and their cry came up to God because of the bondage.

24 So God heard their groaning, and God remembered His **covenant** with Abraham, with Isaac, and with Jacob.

25 And God looked upon the children of Israel, and God **acknowledged** them.

Word Meanings:
1. **content:** satisfied; comfortable
2. **foreign:** strange; away from home
3. **groaned:** suffered; cried loudly
4. **covenant:** promise
5. **acknowledged:** recognized; noticed

Name Meaning:
   Gershom: stranger there

Phrase Meaning:
   in the process of time: what happened as the time passed

Questions:

1. What was Moses content to do? _____

2. Reuel gave something special to Moses. What was it? _____

3. What was the daughter's name? _____

4. What did the daughter give Moses? _____

5. What was his name? _____

6. Why did Moses say this name was given? _____

   _____

7. What happened in the process of time? _____

8. What happened to the children of Israel? _____

   _____

9. Who heard them when they cried out? _____

10. What did God hear? _____

11. What did God remember? _____

12. With whom had God made His covenant? _____

13. What did God do?

   a) _____

   b) _____

DAY FOUR
EXODUS 3:1-4

1 Now Moses was tending the flock of **Jethro** his father-in-law, the priest of Midian. And he led the flock to the back of the desert, and came to Horeb, the mountain of God.

2 And the Angel of the LORD appeared to him in a flame of fire from the midst of a bush. So he looked, and behold, the bush was burning with fire, but the bush was not **consumed**.

3 Then Moses said, "I will now turn aside and see this great sight, why the bush does not burn."

4 So when the LORD saw that he turned aside to look, God called to him from the midst of the bush and said, "Moses, Moses!" And he said, "Here I am."

Word Meanings:
1. **consumed:** used or destroyed
2. **dramatic:** spectacular; exciting
3. **puzzled:** confused; bewildered

Name Meaning:
Jethro: excellence; an honorary title for Reuel

(**Note:** Reuel and Jethro are the same person. Jethro, meaning excellence, was an honorary title for Reuel. See Exodus 2:18 and 3:1.)

Questions:

1. Where was Moses? _____

2. What was Moses' relationship with Jethro? _____

3. What did it tell about who Jethro was? _____

   _____

4. Where did Moses lead the flock? _____

5. What location did Moses come to and what was it called? _____

   _____

6. Who appeared to Moses? _____

7. How did He appear to him? _____

   _____

8. What was unusual about this **dramatic** appearance? _____

   _____

9. What did Moses say? _____

10. What did he desire to see? _____

11. Why was he **puzzled**? _____

12. What did the Lord see? _____

13. What did God do? _____

14. From where did God call him? _____

15. How did Moses respond? _____

DAY FIVE
EXODUS 3:5-8

5 Then He said, "Do not draw near this place. Take your sandals off your feet, for the place where you stand is holy ground."

6 Moreover He said, "I am the God of your father—the God of Abraham, the God of Isaac, and the God of Jacob." And Moses hid his face, for he was afraid to look upon God.

> 7 And the LORD said: "I have surely seen the *oppression* of My people who are in Egypt, and have heard their cry because of their taskmasters, for I know their sorrows.
>
> 8 "So I have come down to deliver them out of the hand of the Egyptians, and to bring them up from that land to a good and large land, to a land flowing with milk and honey, to the place of the Canaanites and the Hittites and the Amorites and the Perizzites and the Hivites and the Jebusites."

Word Meanings:

1. **oppression:** to be under a harsh rule

2. **forefathers:** members of one family; connection by birth

Questions:

1. Who did God say He was? _____

2. Which of Moses' **forefathers** did God mention?

    a) _____

    b) _____

    c) _____

3. What did Moses do? _____

4. What was Moses afraid to do? _____

5. What did the Lord say He had seen? _____

   _____

6. Where were His people living? _____

7. What did the Lord say He had heard? _____

8. Why were the people oppressed? _____

9. What did the Lord know? _____

10. What did the Lord say He had come to do? _____

    _____

11. How did the Lord describe where He would take them?

    a) _____

    b) _____

12. What groups of people did the Lord name that were in this land? _____

    _____

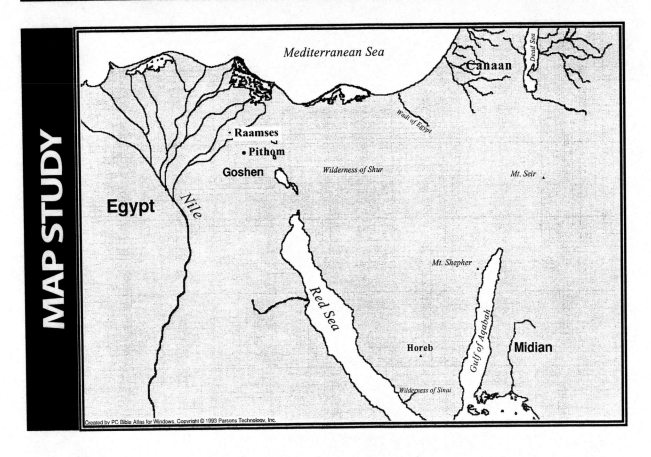

MAP STUDY

Questions:

1. Locate the following and highlight with a marker or colored pencil.

   a) Egypt

   b) Midian

   c) Horeb

2. Draw a blue line to the place Moses went after he killed an Egyptian.

3. Draw the following on your map which identifies the places indicated.

   a) a well beside Midian

   b) a mountain beside Horeb

   c) a burning bush by the mountain where God spoke to Moses

4. Color your map (optional).

REVIEW
LESSON TWO   Exodus 2:11 - 3:8

A. Paraphrase: Write the following in your own words.

1. "Now it came to pass": _____

_____

2. "In the process of time" : _____

_____

B. True (T) or False (F): If the answer is false, write the correct answer below.

_____ 1. When Moses saw an Egyptian beating a Hebrew, he killed the Egyptian.

_____ 2. The priest of Midian had eight daughters.

_____ 3. Moses helped the daughters and watered their flock.

_____ 4. God remembered His covenant to Abraham, Isaac, and Joseph.

_____ 5. Moses was afraid to look on God.

C. Write the correct letter(s) in the blank.

_____ 1. Moses' occupation in Midian was
      a) a priest.
      b) a shepherd.
      c) a farmer.

_____ 2. When Moses encountered the burning bush, he
      a) ran up to get a closer look.
      b) he hurried back to his house.
      c) he turned aside.

_____ 3. When God said who He was, what did Moses do?
      a) He hid his face.
      b) He held up his rod.
      c) He knelt down on the ground.

_____ 4. The Lord said to Moses:
      a) "The Egyptians are My people."
      b) "Come closer to the fire."
      c) "The place where you are standing is holy ground."

DISCOVERY

A DIFFICULT ASSIGNMENT

DAY ONE
EXODUS 3:9-12

9 "Now therefore, behold, the cry of the children of Israel has come to Me, and I have also seen the oppression with which the Egyptians oppress them.

10 "Come now, therefore, and I will send you to Pharaoh that you may bring My people, the children of Israel, out of Egypt."

11 But Moses said to God, "Who am I that I should go to Pharaoh, and that I should bring the children of Israel out of Egypt?"

12 So He said, "I will *certainly* be with you. And this shall be a sign to you that I have sent you: When you have brought the people out of Egypt, you shall serve God on this mountain."

Word Meanings:
1. **certainly:** for sure; without a doubt
2. **plead:** to make an urgent (very important) request
3. **hesitates:** to show uncertainty; to pause before taking action
4. **confirm:** to give proof
5. **assurance:** to give confidence of a promise

Questions:

1. What did God say about the cry of the children of Israel? _____

2. What did He remind Moses that He had seen? _____

   _____

3. How did He **plead** with Moses? _____

   _____

4. What did God say he wanted Moses to do? _____

   _____

5. What small word shows that Moses **hesitates** when God makes this request? _____

6. What three words **confirm** that Moses did not think he was the right choice to go?

   _____

7. What **assurance** did God give Moses? _____

   _____

8. What was Moses supposed to do to show that God had sent him? _____

   _____

   _____

DAY TWO
EXODUS 3:13-15

13 Then Moses said to God, "**Indeed**, when I come to the children of Israel and say to them, 'The God of your fathers has sent me to you,' and they say to me, 'What is His name?' what shall I say to them?"

14 And God said to Moses, "*I AM WHO I AM***." And He said, "Thus you shall say to the children of Israel, 'I AM has sent me to you.'"**

15 Moreover God said to Moses, "**Thus** you shall say to the children of Israel: 'The LORD God of your fathers, the God of Abraham, the God of Isaac, and the God of Jacob, has sent me to you. This is My name forever, and this is My **memorial** to all **generations**.'"

Word Meanings:
1. **indeed:** a certainty; a fact
2. **moreover:** also; besides that
3. **thus:** because of this; as a result
4. **memorial:** remembrance
5. **generations:** the families born from each father

Name Meaning:
I AM WHO I AM: God's name; the living God; YAHWEH (Hebrew)

Questions:

1. What was Moses going to say to the children of Israel? _____

   _____

2. What question did Moses think the people would ask? _____

3. What question did Moses ask God? _____

   _____

4. What did God tell Moses to say? _____

   _____

5. What else did God tell Moses to tell the children of Israel? _____

   _____

6. Who were the fathers? _____

7. What did God say about His name? _____

   _____

DAY THREE
EXODUS 3:16-17

16 "Go and gather the elders of Israel together, and say to them, 'The Lord God of your fathers, the God of Abraham, of Isaac, and of Jacob, appeared to me, saying, "I have surely visited you and seen what is done to you in Egypt;

17 "and I have said I will bring you up out of the **affliction** of Egypt to the land of the Canaanites and the Hittites and the Amorites and the Perizzites and the Hivites and the Jebusites, to **a land flowing with milk and honey**."'"

Word Meanings:
  1. **affliction:** suffering   2. **regarding:** considering

---

Phrase Meaning:
  a land flowing with milk and honey: a wonderfully prosperous (successful, rich) land in which God would provide for their every need

Questions:

1. What did God tell Moses to do? _____

    _____

2. What was he to say to them? _____

    _____

3. Was Moses to tell them who the fathers were? _____

4. What did God tell Moses to say **regarding** what God had done? _____

    _____

5. What did God say He had seen? _____

6. What had God said? _____

    _____

7. To which land would He bring them up? _____

    _____

8. What else did He say about this land? _____

    _____

DAY FOUR

EXODUS 3:18-22

18 "Then they will **heed** your voice; and you **shall** come, you and the elders of Israel, to the king of Egypt; and you shall say to him, 'The LORD God of the Hebrews has met with us; and now, please, let us go three days' journey into the wilderness, that we may sacrifice to the Lord our God.'

19 "But I am sure that the king of Egypt will not let you go, no, not even by a mighty hand.

20 "So I will stretch out My hand and strike Egypt with all My wonders which I will do in its **midst**; and after that he will let you go.

21 "And I will give this people **favor** in the sight of the Egyptians; and it shall be, when you go, that **you shall not go empty-handed**.

22 "But every woman shall ask of her neighbor, **namely**, of her who **dwells** near her house, **articles** of silver, articles of gold, and clothing; and you shall put them on your sons and on your daughters. So you shall **plunder** the Egyptians."

Word Meanings:
1. **heed:** listen to
2. **shall:** will
3. **midst:** in the center or middle (among the Egyptians)
4. **favor:** approval; acceptance
5. **namely:** which is to say
6. **dwells:** lives
7. **articles:** items or objects
8. **plunder:** things taken from an enemy

Phrase Meaning:
you shall not go empty-handed: the Israelites would be given things they would need for their journey by the Egyptians

Questions:

1. What was God sure would happen when Moses took this message to Egypt? _____
   _____

2. Would the king let them go with a mighty hand? _____
   _____

3. What did God say He would do to make it possible for them to leave? _____
   _____

4. With what would this be done? _____

5. Where would these be done?   _____

6. What would the result then be? _____

7. What else would God perform for the people? _____
   _____

8. Why would this benefit the children of Israel? _____
   _____

9. Whom were the women to ask for things? _____
   _____

10. What were they to ask for?

    a) _____

    b) _____

    c) _____

11. How would they carry them? _____
    _____

12. What would they do to the Egyptians? _____

DAY FIVE
EXODUS 4:1-5

> **1** Then Moses answered and said, "But **suppose** they will not believe me or listen to my voice; suppose they say, 'The Lord has not appeared to you.'"
>
> **2** So the Lord said to him, "What is that in your hand?" He said, "A **rod**."
>
> **3** And He said, "**Cast** it on the ground." So he cast it on the ground, and it became a **serpent**; and Moses fled from it.
>
> **4** Then the Lord said to Moses, "Reach out your hand and take it by the tail" (and he reached out his hand and caught it, and it became a rod in his hand),
>
> **5** "that they may believe that the LORD God of their fathers, the God of Abraham, the God of Isaac, and the God of Jacob, has **appeared** to you."

Word Meanings:
1. **suppose:** to think something will happen; "What if...."
2. **rod:** a long stick
3. **cast:** throw
4. **serpent:** snake
5. **appeared:** to come into sight
6. **concerned:** worried
7. **reply:** answer

Questions:

1. About what was Moses **concerned**? _____

   _____

2. What did he think the people might say? _____

   _____

3. With what question did the Lord respond to Moses? _____

   _____

4. What did Moses **reply**? _____

5. What did the Lord say to do with it? _____

6. Did Moses do what God commanded? _____

7. What happened to the rod? _____

8. What did Moses do? _____

9. Then what did the Lord tell Moses to do? _____

   _____

10. What happened?_____

11. Why did the Lord say He had done this? _____

    _____

REVIEW
LESSON THREE   Exodus 3:9 - 4:5

A. Write the correct letter(s) in the blank.

_____ 1. Moses was reluctant to go to Pharaoh because
   a) he liked living in Midian.
   b) he didn't think the people would believe that God had sent him.
   c) he was afraid that Pharaoh would kill him.

_____ 2. God told Moses that Pharaoh would
   a) let the children of Israel leave Egypt.
   b) make the people work harder.
   c) not let the people go, even by a mighty hand.

_____ 3. God assured Moses that He would
   a) send someone to help him if he had problems.
   b) certainly be with him.
   c) give him weapons to help fight the Egyptians.

_____ 4. God promised that
   a) He would show His wonders in Egypt.
   b) He would bring the children of Israel to the land of the Canaanites.
   c) He would gather some elders together to help Moses.

_____ 5. Moses replied to God and said:
   a) "I have a wife and family to take care of."
   b) "Who am I that I should go to Pharaoh?"
   c) "The people will ask, 'What is His name?'"

B. Match the words with their meanings.

_____ 1. certainly   a) to give confidence of a promise

_____ 2. confirm   b) remembrance

_____ 3. assurance   c) to give proof

_____ 4. heed   d) for sure, without a doubt

_____ 5. memorial   e) to listen to

DISCOVERY

GOD'S INSTRUCTIONS TO MOSES

DAY ONE
EXODUS 4:6-9

> **6 Furthermore** the LORD said to him, "Now put your hand in your **bosom**." And he put his hand in his bosom, and when he took it out, **behold**, his hand was **leprous**, like snow.
>
> **7** And He said, "Put your hand in your bosom again." So he put his hand in his bosom again, and drew it out of his bosom, and behold, it was **restored** like his other **flesh**.
>
> **8** "Then it will be, if they do not believe you, nor **heed** the **message** of the first sign, that they may believe the message of the **latter** sign.
>
> **9** "And it shall be, if they do not believe even these two signs, or listen to your voice, that you shall take water from the river and pour it on the dry land. And the water which you take from the river will become blood on the dry land."

Word Meanings:
1. **furthermore:** in addition; besides
2. **bosom:** the front of the human chest
3. **behold:** to see
4. **leprous:** a contagious skin disease which makes the skin white
5. **restored:** to bring back to original condition
6. **flesh:** the tissue of the body
7. **heed:** listen to and act on
8. **message:** information given by one person to another
9. **latter:** the one after the first
10. **reveal:** to show something that has been hidden
11. **compared:** to see a likeness

Questions:

1. What word tells us that the Lord has more to **reveal** to Moses? _____

2. What did the Lord then tell Moses to do? _____

3. What happened when he drew it out? _____

4. To what was it **compared**? _____

5. Then what did the Lord command Moses? _____

   _____

6. Did Moses do as God told him? _____

7. What was the result this time? _____

   _____

8. What reason did God give for giving this second sign? _____

   _____

9.   What should occur if they did not believe these two signs? _____

_____

10. What would God make happen to the water? _____

_____

DAY TWO
EXODUS 4:10-14

> **10** Then Moses said to the LORD, "O my Lord, I am not **eloquent**, neither before nor since You have spoken to Your servant; but I am slow of speech and slow of tongue."
>
> **11** So the LORD said to him, "Who has made man's mouth? Or who makes the **mute**, the **deaf**, the seeing, or the blind? Have not I, the Lord?
>
> **12** "Now therefore, go, and I will be with your mouth and teach you what you shall say."
>
> **13** But he said, "O my Lord, please send by the hand of whomever else You may send."
>
> **14** So the anger of the LORD was kindled against Moses, and He said: "Is not Aaron the Levite your brother? I know that he can speak well. And look, he is also coming out to meet you. When he sees you, he will be glad in his heart."

Word Meanings:
1. **eloquent:** a good and expressive speaker
2. **mute:** cannot speak
3. **deaf:** cannot hear
4. **convince:** persuade; satisfy doubt
5. **qualified:** having the ability for a certain purpose
6. **emotion:** strong feeling
7. **rejection:** refusal

Questions:

1.   What reasons did Moses give to the Lord as to why he should not go to Egypt?

a) _____

b) _____

c) _____

2.   How long did Moses say he had been this way? _____

_____

3.   What did the Lord ask as a reminder to Moses in His response?

a) _____

b) _____

_____

4. What was the Lord's final question to Moses? _____

_____

5. What was the Lord's command to Moses? _____

6. How did God give him confidence with a promise?

      a) _____

      b) _____

7. Did this **convince** Moses that God considered him **qualified**? Explain. _____

_____

8. What **emotion** does the Lord feel at Moses' **rejection**? _____

9. What did the Lord ask Moses about his brother? _____

_____

10. What did the Lord say about him? _____

11. What else did the Lord already know? _____

_____

12. How did the Lord say Aaron would feel? _____

DAY THREE EXODUS 4:15-20	15 "Now you shall speak to him and put the words in his mouth. And I will be with your mouth and with his mouth, and I will teach you what you shall do. 16 "So he shall be your **spokesman** to the people. And he himself shall be as a mouth for you, and you shall be to him as God. 17 "And you shall take this rod in your hand, with which you shall do the **signs**." 18 So Moses went and returned to Jethro his father-in-law, and said to him, "Please let me go and return to my brethren who are in Egypt, and see whether they are still alive." And Jethro said to Moses, "Go in peace." 19 And the LORD said to Moses in Midian, "Go, return to Egypt; for all the men who sought your life are dead." 20 Then Moses took his wife and his sons and set them on a donkey, and he returned to the land of Egypt. And Moses took the rod of God in his hand.

Word Meanings:
1. **spokesman:** one who speaks for another
2. **signs:** warnings or evidence that they (the Egyptians) should listen to what Moses told them God had said
3. **conversation:** talking with another
4. **allowance:** something permitted; an adjustment
5. **permission:** to agree that someone may do something

Questions:

1. What did the Lord tell Moses to do? _____

   _____

2. Who would control their **conversation**? _____

   _____

3. What did the Lord say He would do? _____

4. What **allowance** did the Lord make for Moses? _____

   _____

5. What would Moses be to Aaron? _____

6. What would Moses take with him to Egypt? _____

7. What was he to do with this? _____

   _____

8. Where did Moses go? _____

   _____

9. What did he ask Jethro? _____

   _____

10. Did Jethro give his **permission**? _____

11. Why was it safe for Moses to return to Egypt? _____

   _____

12. Who returned to Egypt with Moses? _____

13. What else did Moses take with him? _____

   _____

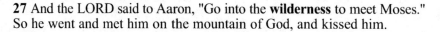

DAY FOUR	**27** And the LORD said to Aaron, "Go into the **wilderness** to meet Moses." So he went and met him on the mountain of God, and kissed him.

DAY FOUR
EXODUS 4:27-31

27 And the LORD said to Aaron, "Go into the **wilderness** to meet Moses." So he went and met him on the mountain of God, and kissed him.

28 So Moses told Aaron all the words of the LORD who had sent him, and all the signs which He had commanded him.

29 Then Moses and Aaron went and gathered together all the elders of the children of Israel.

30 And Aaron spoke all the words which the LORD had spoken to Moses. Then he did the signs in the sight of the people.

31 So the people believed; and when they heard that the LORD had *visited* the children of Israel and that He had looked on their *affliction*, then they bowed their heads and worshiped.

Word Meanings:
1. **wilderness:** an area of land that is not inhabited
2. **visited:** came to see
3. **affliction:** suffering
4. **communicate:** to give information or tell something

Questions:

1. What did the Lord say to Aaron? _____

   _____

2. Did Aaron obey the Lord? _____

3. Where did they meet? _____

4. What did Aaron do when he met Moses? _____

5. What did Moses **communicate** to Aaron?

   a) _____

   b) _____

6. What did Moses and Aaron do next? _____

   _____

7. Who spoke all the words that the Lord had given? _____

8. Then what did Aaron do? _____

   _____

9. What happened when the people heard God's words and saw His signs? _____

   _____

10. What was the response of the people when they heard that the Lord had visited them and

    had looked on their affliction? _____

    _____

DAY FIVE

EXODUS 5:1-5

1 Afterward Moses and Aaron went in and told Pharaoh, "Thus says the LORD God of Israel: 'Let My people go, that they may hold a **feast** to Me in the wilderness.'"

2 And Pharaoh said, "Who is the LORD, that I should **obey** His voice to let Israel go? I do not know the LORD, nor will I let Israel go."

3 So they said, "The God of the Hebrews has met with us. Please, let us go three days' journey into the desert and **sacrifice** to the LORD our God, lest He fall upon us with **pestilence** or with the sword."

4 Then the king of Egypt said to them, "Moses and Aaron, why do you take the people from their work? Get back to your labor."

5 And Pharaoh said, "Look, the people of the land are many now, and you make them rest from their labor!"

Word Meanings:
1. **feast:** religious remembrance
2. **obey:** to follow a command
3. **sacrifice:** offering to God
4. **pestilence:** a deadly disease

Questions:

1. What did Moses and Aaron tell Pharaoh? _____

   _____

2. What reason was given to Pharaoh for this request? _____

   _____

3. What was Pharaoh's response? _____

   _____

4. What else did he say about the Lord? _____

5. Would he allow the people to go? _____

   _____

6. Moses and Aaron gave further reason for the departure of the people. Tell what they said.

   _____

7. How far did they want to take the people into the desert? _____

8. What did they tell Pharaoh they would do in the desert? _____

   _____

9. What would result if they failed? _____

   _____

10. How did Pharaoh ignore their request instead of answering?_____

    _____

11. Of what did he accuse Moses and Aaron?_____

    _____

REVIEW
LESSON FOUR　　　Exodus 4:6 - 5:5

A. Complete the following.

1. The Lord said to Moses: "What is that in your _____?"

2. Moses answered: "A _____."

3. Moses cast it on the _____,

4. and it became a _____.

5. The Lord said, "Put your hand in your _____."

6. When Moses took it out, behold, his _____

7. was leprous, like _____.

8. The Lord said, "Then it will be, if they do not _____ you,

9. nor heed the message of the _____ sign,

10. that they may believe the message of the _____ sign."

B. True (T) or False (F): If the answer is false, cross out the word that is wrong and write the correct answer.

_____ 1. The Lord gave Moses three signs to show that He had sent him.

_____ 2. Moses wanted to go immediately to Egypt and set his people free.

_____ 3. The Lord sent the elders to help Moses speak to Pharaoh.

_____ 4. Moses asked his father-in-law for permission to return to Egypt.

_____ 5. Aaron met Moses in Egypt.

DISCOVERY

MOSES CONFRONTS PHARAOH

DAY ONE
EXODUS 6:1-5

1 Then the LORD said to Moses, "Now you shall see what I will do to Pharaoh. For with **a strong hand** he will let them go, and with a strong hand he will drive them out of his land."

2 And God spoke to Moses and said to him: "I am the LORD.

3 "I appeared to Abraham, to Isaac, and to Jacob, as God Almighty, but by My name LORD I was not known to them.

4 "I have also *established* **My** *covenant* **with them, to give them the land of Canaan, the land of their** *pilgrimage*, **in which they were strangers.**

5 "And I have also heard the groaning of the children of Israel whom the Egyptians keep in bondage, and I have remembered My covenant."

Word Meanings:
1. **established:** settled securely
2. **covenant:** the agreement God had made to His people
3. **pilgrimage:** journey

Phrase Meaning:
a strong hand: power that would use force

Questions:

1. What did the Lord tell Moses that he would see? _____

   _____

2. With a strong hand, what would Pharaoh do?

   a) _____

   b) _____

3. Who did God say He was? _____

4. Whom had He appeared to as God Almighty?

   a) _____

   b) _____

   c) _____

5. What was not known to them? _____

6. What had He established with them? _____

7. What was His covenant? _____

8. What was this land? _____

9. What were they in this land? _____

10. What had the Lord heard? _____

    _____

11. Who had kept the people in bondage? _____

12. What had the Lord remembered? _____

DAY TWO

EXODUS 6:6-9

6 "Therefore say to the children of Israel: 'I am the LORD; I will bring you out from under the burdens of the Egyptians, I will **rescue** you from their bondage, and I will **redeem** you with **an outstretched arm** and **with great judgments**.

7 'I will take you as My people, and I will be your God. Then you shall know that I am the LORD your God who brings you out from under the burdens of the Egyptians.

8 'And I will bring you into the land which I **swore** to give to Abraham, Isaac, and Jacob; and I will give it to you as a **heritage**: I am the LORD.'"

9 So Moses spoke thus to the children of Israel; but they did not heed Moses, because of **anguish of spirit** and cruel bondage.

Word Meanings:
1. **rescue:** make free; save
2. **redeem:** carry out; fulfill God's promise to set them free
3. **swore:** promised by oath
4. **heritage:** inheritance
5. **relate:** tell; report

Phrase Meanings:
1. **an outstretched arm:** with loving compassion
2. **with great judgments:** what the Lord would do to Egypt as a result of their sin and unbelief
3. **anguish of spirit:** loss of energy because of pain and suffering (Today, we may call this depression.)

Questions:

1. What five things did God say that Moses was to **relate** to the children of Israel?

    a) _____

    b) _____

    _____

c) _____

_____

d) _____

e) _____

2. What did He want the people to know? _____

_____

3. What else did the Lord promise? _____

_____

4. What would this land be to them? _____

5. Why did the people not heed what Moses told them?

a) _____

b) _____

DAY THREE
EXODUS 7:1-6

1 So the LORD said to Moses: "See, I have made you as God to Pharaoh, and Aaron your brother shall be your **prophet**.

2 "You shall speak all that I command you. And Aaron your brother shall tell Pharaoh to send the children of Israel out of his land.

3 "And I will **harden Pharaoh's heart**, and multiply My signs and My wonders in the land of Egypt.

4 "But Pharaoh will not heed you, so that I may lay My hand on Egypt and bring My armies and My people, the children of Israel, out of the land of Egypt by great judgments.

5 "And the Egyptians shall know that I am the LORD, when I stretch out My hand on Egypt and bring out the children of Israel from among them."

6 Then Moses and Aaron did so; just as the LORD commanded them, so they did.

Word Meanings:
1. **prophet:** one who speaks for God

2. **rebellion:** defiance and resistance (refusal to listen to God)

Phrase Meaning:
harden Pharaoh's heart: make him unwilling; difficult

Questions:

1. What did the Lord tell Moses to speak to Pharaoh? _____

_____

2. What would Aaron do? _____

_____

3. What would happen to Pharaoh's heart? _____

4. What did God say He would multiply? _____

5. Where would this happen? _____

6. Would Pharaoh heed the words of Aaron? _____

7. What would happen because of Pharaoh's **rebellion**? _____

_____

8. Whom would the Lord bring out of Egypt? _____

_____

9. Who would know that "I am the LORD"? _____

10. What would the Lord do?

    a) _____

    b) _____

11. What did Moses and Aaron do? _____

_____

DAY FOUR
EXODUS 7:8-13

8 Then the LORD spoke to Moses and Aaron, saying,

9 "When Pharaoh speaks to you, saying, 'Show a miracle for yourselves,' then you shall say to Aaron, 'Take your rod and cast it before Pharaoh, and let it become a serpent.'"

10 So Moses and Aaron went in to Pharaoh, and they did so, just as the Lord commanded. And Aaron cast down his rod before Pharaoh and before his servants, and it became a serpent.

11 But Pharaoh also called the **wise men** and the **sorcerers**; so the magicians of Egypt, they also did in like manner with their **enchantments**.

12 For every man threw down his rod, and they became serpents. But Aaron's rod swallowed up their rods.

13 And Pharaoh's heart grew hard, and he did not heed them, as the LORD had said.

Word Meanings:

1. **wise men:** men who had studied events and could understand why things happened
2. **sorcerers:** evil magicians
3. **enchantments:** to put under a magic spell
4. **demand:** to ask with authority (one who has the right to command)

Questions:

1. What did the Lord tell Moses and Aaron that Pharaoh would **demand**? _____

   _____

2. What would Aaron do? _____

3. What would happen? _____

4. Whom did Pharaoh call?_____

   _____

5. What did these men do? _____

   _____

6. How did they do it? _____

7. What did Aaron's rod do? _____

8. What happened to Pharaoh's heart? _____

9. Who had told Moses and Aaron that Pharaoh would not heed them? _____

DAY FIVE

EXODUS 7:19-22

19 Then the LORD spoke to Moses, "Say to Aaron, 'Take your rod and stretch out your hand over the waters of Egypt, over their streams, over their rivers, over their ponds, and over all their pools of water, that they may become blood. And there shall be blood throughout all the land of Egypt, both in buckets of wood and pitchers of stone.'"

20 And Moses and Aaron did so, just as the LORD commanded. So he lifted up the rod and struck the waters that were in the river, in the sight of Pharaoh and in the sight of his servants. And all the waters that were in the river were turned to blood.

21 The fish that were in the river died, the river stank, and the Egyptians could not drink the water of the river. So there was blood throughout all the land of Egypt.

22 Then the magicians of Egypt did so with their enchantments; and Pharaoh's heart grew hard, and he did not heed them, as the LORD had said.

Word Meanings:

1. **duplicate:** do the same thing
2. **disaster:** something terrible that happens

Phrase Meaning:
  bodies of water: areas in which water is found

Questions:

1. After the Lord spoke to Moses, what did he tell Aaron to do with his rod? _____

    _____

2. Which **bodies of water** are mentioned?

    a) _____

    b) _____

    c) _____

    d) _____

3. What would result when Aaron did as the Lord commanded? _____

    _____

4. Where else would the water become blood?

    a) _____

    b) _____

5. What happened?_____

6. What was the result of the water becoming blood?

    a) _____

    b) _____

    c) _____

7. Were the magicians of Egypt able to **duplicate** this **disaster** with their enchantments?

    _____

8. What happened to Pharaoh's heart? _____

9. Did Pharaoh listen to Moses and what the Lord said? _____

Exodus 6 - 7

A. Match the words with their meanings.

_____ 1. covenant   (a) one who speaks for God

_____ 2. rescue   (b) do the same thing

_____ 3. swore   (c) the agreement God had made to His people

_____ 4. prophet   (d) evil magicians

_____ 5. sorcerers   (e) make free; save

_____ 6. duplicate   (f) promised by oath

B. Multiple Choice: Write the correct letter(s) in the blank.

_____ 1. God predicted
            a) that Pharaoh would pay the Israelites to stay in Egypt.
            b) that Pharaoh would drive them out of the land.
            c) that Pharaoh's heart would be hard.

_____ 2. Which of these signs did Moses give Pharaoh in these chapters?
            a) rod into a serpent
            b) extreme cold and heat
            c) water changed to blood
            d) bugs and flies

_____ 3. The results of these wonders were
            a) many people died from drinking the water.
            b) the fish died.
            c) the river stank.

_____ 4. The waters turned to blood in the
            a) drinking fountains.
            b) streams and ponds.
            c) water in Goshen.
            d) rivers.

 DISCOVERY

PHARAOH'S REBELLION AGAINST GOD

DAY ONE
EXODUS 8:1-7

1 And the LORD spoke to Moses, "Go to Pharaoh and say to him, 'Thus says the LORD: "Let My people go, that they may serve Me.

2 "But if you **refuse** to let them go, behold, I will **smite** all your **territory** with frogs.

3 "So the river shall bring forth frogs abundantly, which shall go up and come into your house, into your bedroom, on your bed, into the houses of your servants, on your people, into your ovens, and into your **kneading bowls**.

4 "And the frogs shall come up on you, on your people, and on all your servants."'"

5 Then the LORD spoke to Moses, "Say to Aaron, 'Stretch out your hand with your rod over the streams, over the rivers, and over the ponds, and cause frogs to come up on the land of Egypt.'"

6 So Aaron stretched out his hand over the waters of Egypt, and the frogs came up and covered the land of Egypt.

7 And the magicians did so with their enchantments, and brought up frogs on the land of Egypt.

Word Meanings:
1. **refuse:** not allow
2. **smite:** to make a powerful effect
3. **territory:** area of land
4. **consequence:** a result after an action is taken

Phrase Meaning:
kneading bowls: containers in which bread dough is mixed

Questions:

1. To whom did the Lord speak? _____

2. What message did He want sent to Pharaoh? _____

   _____

3. What **consequence** would follow if Pharaoh refused?_____

   _____

4.   Where would these creatures come from? _____

5.   Where did He say they would go?

        a) _____

        b) _____

        c) _____

        d) _____

        e) _____

        f) _____

        g) _____

6.   Who would be affected?

        a) _____

        b) _____

        c) _____

7.   Were the children of Israel mentioned?_____

8.   What did the Lord tell Moses? _____

_____

9.   What would happen when Aaron obeyed? _____

_____

10. When did the frogs come up and cover the land? _____

_____

11. Were the magicians able to produce the same result with their enchantments? _____

DAY TWO
EXODUS 8:8-15

8 Then Pharaoh called for Moses and Aaron, and said, "**Entreat** the LORD that He may take away the frogs from me and from my people; and I will let the people go, that they may sacrifice to the LORD."

9 And Moses said to Pharaoh, "Accept the honor of saying when I shall **intercede** for you, for your servants, and for your people, to destroy the frogs from you and your houses, that they may remain in the river only."

10 So he said, "Tomorrow." And he said, "Let it be according to your word, that you may know that there is no one like the LORD our God.

11 "And the frogs shall depart from you, from your houses, from your servants, and from your people. They shall remain in the river only."

12 Then Moses and Aaron went out from Pharaoh. And Moses cried out to the LORD concerning the frogs which He had brought against Pharaoh.

13 So the LORD did according to the word of Moses. And the frogs died out of the houses, out of the courtyards, and out of the fields.

14 They gathered them together in **heaps**, and the land stank.

15 But when Pharaoh saw that there was **relief**, he hardened his heart and did not heed them, as the LORD had said.

Word Meanings:

1. **entreat:** to ask with persuasion (be convincing)
2. **intercede:** to plead or make a request for someone else
3. **heaps:** piles
4. **relief:** to stop the cause of pain or suffering
5. **responsible:** to be dependent upon to make something happen
6. **accomplishing:** being successful in doing something

Questions:

1. What did Pharaoh ask Moses and Aaron to do? _____

   _____

2. What did Pharaoh promise to do if the frogs were taken away? _____

   _____

3. What did Moses tell Pharaoh he had the honor of doing? _____

   _____

4. What would Moses ask from the Lord? _____

   _____

5. When did Pharaoh wish this to happen? _____

6. Who did Moses want Pharaoh to know was **responsible** for **accomplishing** this? _____

   _____

7. By whose power would the frogs be gone from the land? _____

   _____

8. Did Moses tell Pharaoh what would happen? _____

   _____

9. For what reason did Moses entreat the Lord? _____

   _____

10. Did the Lord hear Moses' request? _____

   _____

11. What did they do with all the frogs? _____

12. What did Pharaoh do when he saw that there was relief? _____

_____

DAY THREE
EXODUS 8:16-19

16 So the LORD said to Moses, "Say to Aaron, 'Stretch out your rod, and strike the dust of the land, so that it may become **lice** throughout all the land of Egypt.'"

17 And they did so. For Aaron stretched out his hand with his rod and struck the dust of the earth, and it became lice on man and beast. All the dust of the land became lice throughout all the land of Egypt.

18 Now the magicians so worked with their enchantments to bring forth lice, but they could not. So there were lice on man and beast.

19 Then the magicians said to Pharaoh, "This is the **finger of God**." But Pharaoh's heart grew hard, and he did not heed them, just as the LORD had said.

Word Meaning:
   lice: many small insects that suck blood

Phrase Meaning:
   finger of God: this is what God has done; no man can do this

Questions:

1. What did the Lord make happen to the land of Egypt when Aaron stretched out his rod this time? _____

2. Where did the lice go? _____

3. Were the magicians able to do the same thing this time? _____

4. What did the magicians tell Pharaoh? _____

_____

5. Did Pharaoh listen? _____

6. Who had already said that Pharaoh would not listen? _____

DAY FOUR
EXODUS 8:20-24

20 And the LORD said to Moses, "Rise early in the morning and stand before Pharaoh as he comes out to the water. Then say to him, 'Thus says the LORD: "Let My people go, that they may serve Me.

21 "Or else, if you will not let My people go, behold, I will send **swarms** of flies on you and your servants, on your people and into your houses. The houses of the Egyptians shall be full of swarms of flies, and also the ground on which they stand.

22 "And in that day I will **set apart the land** of Goshen, in which My people dwell, that no swarms of flies shall be there, in order that you may know that I am the LORD in the midst of the land.

23 "I will make a difference between My people and your people. Tomorrow this sign shall be."'"

24 And the LORD did so. Thick swarms of flies came into the house of Pharaoh, into his servants' houses, and into all the land of Egypt. The land was **corrupted** because of the swarms of flies.

Word Meanings:
1. **swarms:** large numbers of insects on the move

2. **corrupted:** spoiled

Phrase Meaning:
set apart the land: to protect from the disaster

Questions:

1. What did Moses again say to Pharaoh? _____

_____

2. What would be the consequence if Pharaoh refused? _____

_____

3. What would happen in the land of Goshen, where God's people lived?_____

_____

4. What reason did God give for doing this?_____

_____

5. What did the Lord say He would do?_____

_____

6. When would this take place? _____

_____

7. Did it happen just as the Lord said? _____

_____

8. What resulted from the swarms of flies? _____

DAY FIVE
EXODUS 8:25-32

> **25** Then Pharaoh called for Moses and Aaron, and said, "Go, **sacrifice** to your God in the land."
>
> **26** And Moses said, "It is not right to do so, for we would be **sacrificing the abomination** of the Egyptians to the LORD our God. If we sacrifice the **abomination** of the Egyptians **before their eyes**, then will they not **stone us**?
>
> **27** "We will go three days' journey into the wilderness and sacrifice to the LORD our God as He will command us."
>
> **28** And Pharaoh said, "I will let you go, that you may sacrifice to the LORD your God in the wilderness; only you shall not go very far away. Intercede for me."
>
> **29** Then Moses said, "Indeed I am going out from you, and I will entreat the LORD, that the swarms of flies may depart tomorrow from Pharaoh, from his servants, and from his people. But let Pharaoh not **deal deceitfully** anymore in not letting the people go to sacrifice to the LORD."
>
> **30** So Moses went out from Pharaoh and entreated the LORD.
>
> **31** And the LORD did according to the word of Moses; He removed the swarms of flies from Pharaoh, from his servants, and from his people. Not one remained.
>
> **32** But Pharaoh hardened his heart at this time also; neither would he let the people go.

Word Meanings:
1. **sacrifice:** to offer something to the Lord
2. **abomination:** something extremely offensive; hated
3. **permission:** to let (allow) them to do as requested
4. **condition:** something required as part of an agreement—"I will let you go, but only if you don't go far."

Phrase Meanings:
1. **sacrificing the abomination:** the Egyptians hated the worship of the Israelites
2. **before their eyes:** sacrificing where they could be seen by the Egyptians
3. **stone us:** a method of killing people
4. **deal deceitfully:** handle or treat dishonestly (to not do what is promised)

Questions:

1. What did Pharaoh say when he called for Moses and Aaron? _____

    _____

2. Why was Moses not happy to have Pharaoh's **permission**? _____

    _____

3. What did Moses say would happen if they stayed in the land "before their eyes" to sacrifice?

    _____

4. What did Moses say they would do?

    a) _____

    b) _____

5. Did Pharaoh agree to this? _____

6. What was the **condition** Pharaoh made? _____

    _____

7. Then what did Pharaoh ask Moses? _____

8. What did Moses tell Pharaoh he would do? _____

    _____

9. What warning did Moses give Pharaoh? _____

    _____

    _____

10. What happened when Moses entreated the Lord? _____

    _____

11. Did any flies remain? _____

12. Did Pharaoh keep his word to Moses and the Lord? _____

    _____

REVIEW
LESSON SIX

Exodus 8

A. Write the correct letter(s) in the blank.

_____ 1. The meaning of the word sacrifice is
   a) to not let someone do what they want.
   b) to offer something to the Lord.
   c) to give an opinion.

_____ 2. The meaning of the word consequence is
   a) asking for permission.
   b) doing something you were told not to do.
   c) a result after an action is taken.

_____ 3. The meaning of the word entreat is
   a) to make a statement.
   b) to ask and try to convince.
   c) to demand something.

_____ 4. Who asked the Lord to take away the frogs?
   a) Moses
   b) Pharaoh
   c) Aaron

_____ 5. Who had the power to remove the frogs from the land?
   a) Moses
   b) the magicians
   c) the Lord

_____ 6. What happened after Moses entreated the Lord?
   a) The frogs died.
   b) The frogs were gathered together in heaps.
   c) Pharaoh decided to let the people go.

_____ 7. The meaning of the word abomination is
   a) an offering.
   b) an agreement.
   c) something hated.

_____ 8. The reason Moses gave Pharaoh for leaving Egypt was
   a) to sacrifice to the Lord.
   b) to go camping.
   c) to get away from the flies.
   d) to go to Disneyland.

B. Complete the following from Exodus 8:20-24.

Thus says the LORD: "Let My _____ go, that they may _____ Me.

I will make a _____ between My people and _____ people."

DISCOVERY

BY GOD'S POWER

DAY ONE
EXODUS 9:1-7

1 Then the LORD said to Moses, "Go in to Pharaoh and tell him, 'Thus says the LORD God of the Hebrews: "Let My people go, that they may serve Me.

2 "For if you refuse to let them go, and still hold them,

3 "behold, the hand of the LORD will be on your cattle in the field, on the horses, on the donkeys, on the camels, on the oxen, and on the sheep— a very severe **pestilence**.

4 "And the LORD will make a difference between the **livestock** of Israel and the livestock of Egypt. So nothing shall die of all that belongs to the children of Israel."'"

5 Then the LORD appointed a set time, saying, "Tomorrow the LORD will do this thing in the land."

6 So the LORD did this thing on the next day, and all the livestock of Egypt died; but of the livestock of the children of Israel, not one died.

7 Then Pharaoh sent, and indeed, not even one of the livestock of the Israelites was dead. But the heart of Pharaoh became hard, and he did not let the people go.

Word Meanings:
1. **pestilence:** a deadly, infectious, and rapidly-spreading disease
2. **livestock:** domestic animals raised for use or profit
3. **confirm:** to give proof
4. **condition:** state of being

Questions:

1. What was the repeated command the Lord gave to Pharaoh? _____

   _____

2. Which animals in Egypt would be affected by a severe pestilence?

   a) _____   d) _____

   b) _____   e) _____

   c) _____   f) _____

3. What would the Lord do in regards to the livestock of Israel and Egypt?

    a) _____

    b) _____

4. When did the Lord set the time that this would happen? _____

5. Did everything happen exactly as the Lord had said? _____

6. What did Pharaoh do to **confirm** what had happened to the Israelites' livestock?

    _____

7. Did any of the Israelites' livestock die? _____

8. What was the **condition** of Pharaoh's heart? _____

9. What would he not do? _____

DAY TWO
EXODUS 9:8-12

8 So the LORD said to Moses and Aaron, "Take for yourselves handfuls of ashes from a furnace, and let Moses scatter it toward the heavens in the sight of Pharaoh.

9 "And it will become fine dust in all the land of Egypt, and it will cause boils that break out in sores on man and beast throughout all the land of Egypt."

10 Then they took ashes from the furnace and stood before Pharaoh, and Moses scattered them toward heaven. And they caused boils that break out in sores on man and beast.

11 And the magicians could not stand before Moses because of the boils, for the boils were on the magicians and on all the Egyptians.

12 But the LORD hardened the heart of Pharaoh; and he did not heed them, just as the LORD had spoken to Moses.

Questions:

1. What did the Lord tell Moses and Aaron? _____

    _____

2. What did He tell Moses to do with this? _____

3. In whose sight would Moses do this? _____

4. What would the ashes become? _____

5. Where would this take place? _____

6. What would the result be? _____

    _____

7.   Did this happen as the Lord said? _____

8.   Who could not stand before Moses and why? _____

_____

9.   What did the Lord do? _____

_____

10. What would Pharaoh not do? _____

DAY THREE

EXODUS 9:13-17

13 Then the LORD said to Moses, "Rise early in the morning and stand before Pharaoh, and say to him, 'Thus says the LORD God of the Hebrews: "Let My people go, that they may serve Me,

14 "for at this time I will send all My **plagues** to your very heart, and on your servants and on your people, that you may know that there is none like Me in all the earth.

15 "Now if I had stretched out My hand and struck you and your people with pestilence, then you would have been cut off from the earth.

16 "But indeed for this *purpose* **I have raised you up, that I may show My power in you, and that My name may be declared in all the earth.**

17 "As yet you *exalt* **yourself against My people in that you will not let them go."'"

Word Meanings:
1. **plagues:** terrible disasters
2. **purpose:** reason
3. **exalt:** make oneself great

Questions:

1.   What command did the Lord repeat? _____

_____

2.   Where would the Lord send plagues at this time? _____

3.   Who else would be affected?

a) _____

b) _____

4.   What did the Lord want them to know? _____

_____

5.   What did the Lord say He could have done if He had stretched out His hand? _____

_____

6.   What would have resulted? _____

_____

7.   Which words tell us that the Lord did not actually do this? _____

8.   For what purpose had the Lord raised up Pharaoh?

a)   _____

b)   _____

9.   Where would the Lord's name be declared? _____

10. What did the Lord say that Pharaoh was continuing to do?   _____

_____

DAY FOUR
EXODUS 9:18-26

18 "Behold, tomorrow about this time I will cause very heavy **hail** to rain down, such as has not been in Egypt since its **founding** until now.

19 "Therefore send now and gather your livestock and all that you have in the field, for the hail shall come down on every man and every animal which is found in the field and is not brought home; and they shall die."

20 He who **feared the word of the LORD** among the servants of Pharaoh made his servants and his livestock flee to the houses.

21 But he who did not regard the word of the LORD left his servants and his livestock in the field.

22 Then the LORD said to Moses, "Stretch out your hand toward heaven, that there may be hail in all the land of Egypt—on man, on beast, and on every **herb** of the field, throughout the land of Egypt."

23 And Moses stretched out his rod toward heaven; and the LORD sent thunder and hail, and **fire darted to the ground**. And the LORD rained hail on the land of Egypt.

24 So there was hail, and fire **mingled** with the hail, so very heavy that there was none like it in all the land of Egypt since it became a **nation**.

25 And the hail struck throughout the whole land of Egypt, all that was in the field, both man and beast; and the hail struck every herb of the field and broke every tree of the field.

26 Only in the land of Goshen, where the children of Israel were, there was no hail.

Word Meanings:
1. **hail:** rain drops that have turned into ice
2. **founding:** when it began
3. **herb:** plants used for medicine and spices for food
4. **mingled:** mixed with
5. **nation:** large number of people under one government
6. **extensive:** amount of area affected by something
7. **devastation:** extreme destruction

Phrase Meanings:
  1. **feared the word of the LORD:** believed that the Lord would do what He said
  2. **fire darted to the ground:** lightning striking the earth

Questions:

1. What did the Lord say would happen the next day? _____

    _____

2. Had anything like this ever happened before in Egypt? _____

3. What instructions did the Lord give? _____

    _____

4. What warning did the Lord give? _____

    _____

5. What did those who feared the Lord do? _____

6. What did those who did not regard the word of the Lord do? _____

    _____

7. What did the Lord tell Moses to do? _____

8. How **extensive** would the plague of the hail be? _____

    _____

9. Whom and what would the hail affect?

    a) _____

    b) _____

    c) _____

10. What did Moses stretch toward heaven? _____

11. What did this cause to happen? _____

12. What else happened? _____

13. Complete the following which tells of the **devastation** in the land of Egypt:

    "So there was _____, and _____ mingled with the _____."

14. What resulted from this disaster?

    a) _____

    _____

    b) _____

    c) _____

15. Which land was protected from the hail? _____

16. Who lived in this land? _____

DAY FIVE
EXODUS 9:27-35

27 And Pharaoh sent and called for Moses and Aaron, and said to them, "I have **sinned** this time. The LORD is **righteous**, and my people and I are **wicked**.

28 "Entreat the LORD, that there may be no more mighty thundering and hail, for it is enough. I will let you go, and you shall stay no longer."

29 So Moses said to him, "As soon as I have gone out of the city, I will spread out my hands to the LORD; the thunder will cease, and there will be no more hail, that you may know that the earth is the LORD's.

30 "But as for you and your servants, I know that you will not yet fear the LORD God."

31 Now the **flax** and the **barley** were struck, for the barley was in the head and the flax was in bud.

32 But the **wheat** and the **spelt** were not struck, for they are late crops.

33 So Moses went out of the city from Pharaoh and spread out his hands to the LORD; then the thunder and the hail ceased, and the rain was not poured on the earth.

34 And when Pharaoh saw that the rain, the hail, and the thunder had ceased, he sinned yet more; and he hardened his heart, he and his servants.

35 So the heart of Pharaoh was hard; neither would he let the children of Israel go, as the LORD had spoken by Moses.

Word Meanings:
1. **sinned:** went against God and His law
2. **righteous:** morally good; pure
3. **wicked:** very bad; evil
4. **flax:** a plant which produces fiber for cloth
5. **barley:** grain used for food
6. **wheat:** grain used for flour
7. **spelt:** an ancient wheat
8. **confession:** to admit a wrong
9. **admitted:** to tell someone you have done wrong
10. **regarding:** what something said is about

Questions:

1. What was Pharaoh's **confession** to Moses and Aaron? _____

2. Was this the first time he had **admitted** to doing anything wrong? _____

3. What did Pharaoh say **regarding** the Lord? _____

4. What did Pharaoh say about his people and himself? _____

   _____

5. What did Pharaoh want Moses to do? _____

6. What did he want to stop? _____

7. What did he promise to do? _____

8. Did Moses agree to Pharaoh's request?_____

9. What reason did he give? _____

    _____

10. But what did Moses know about Pharaoh and his servants? _____

    _____

11. What was told about the crops?

    a) _____

    _____

    b) _____

    _____

12. What happened again when the hail stopped? _____

    _____

    _____

REVIEW
LESSON SEVEN   Exodus 9

A. Write the correct letter(s) in the blank.

_____ 1. The Lord said:
  a) "Let My people go that they may serve Me."
  b) "I will send a severe pestilence in Egypt next week."
  c) "Only the camels will be affected."

_____ 2. The Lord instructed Moses and Aaron to
  a) take the rod and visit Pharaoh to tell him what would happen.
  b) take handfuls of ashes from a furnace.
  c) scatter the ashes toward the heavens.

_____ 3. The Lord wanted the Egyptians to know
  a) that He had the power to make them sick.
  b) that they must keep their houses clean.
  c) that there is none like Him in all the earth.

_____ 4. What does the phrase "feared the Lord" mean?
  a) to be scared because the Lord wants to be cruel to people
  b) to know and believe that the Lord will do what He says
  c) to hide from the Lord because he doesn't love people

_____ 5. What did Pharaoh say about the Lord?
  a) "I have sinned."
  b) "I will let the people go."
  c) "He is righteous."

B. Complete the following from Exodus 9:4.

"And the _____ will make a _____ between the livestock of _____
and the livestock of _____. So nothing shall die of all that belongs to the children of
_____."

C. Match the words with their meanings.

_____ 1. sin   a) to admit you have done wrong

_____ 2. confession   b) to do wrong; to violate God's laws

DISCOVERY

GOD'S FINAL WARNING TO PHARAOH

DAY ONE
EXODUS 10:3-7

> **3** So Moses and Aaron came in to Pharaoh and said to him, "Thus says the LORD God of the Hebrews: 'How long will you refuse to **humble** yourself before Me? Let My people go, that they may serve Me.
>
> **4** 'Or else, if you refuse to let My people go, behold, tomorrow I will bring **locusts** into your territory.
>
> **5** 'And they shall cover the face of the earth, so that no one will be able to see the earth; and they shall eat the **residue** of what is left, which remains to you from the hail, and they shall eat every tree which grows up for you out of the field.
>
> **6** 'They shall fill your houses, the houses of all your servants, and the houses of all the Egyptians—which neither your fathers nor your fathers' fathers have seen, since the day that they were on the earth to this day.' " And he turned and went out from Pharaoh.
>
> **7** Then Pharaoh's servants said to him, "How long shall this man be a **snare** to us? Let the men go, that they may serve the LORD their God. Do you not yet know that Egypt is destroyed?"

Word Meanings:
1. **humble:** to lower the position of oneself to another
2. **locusts:** large grasshoppers that cause destruction to crops
3. **residue:** that which is left over
4. **snare:** a trap that brings suffering to those caught in it
5. **describe:** to tell in words what something is like
6. **recommendation:** an advisement or suggestion
7. **rebuke:** an expression of strong disapproval

Questions:

1. **Describe** the next plague that was sent to Pharaoh. _____

   _____

2. What would occur when this plague came?

   a) _____

   _____

   b) _____

3. What question did Pharaoh's servants ask him? _____

   _____

4.   What was their **recommendation** to Pharaoh? _____

_____

5.   What was their **rebuke** to Pharaoh? _____

_____

DAY TWO
EXODUS 10:8-11

8 So Moses and Aaron were brought again to Pharaoh, and he said to them, "Go, serve the LORD your God. Who are the ones that are going?"

9 And Moses said, "We will go with our young and our old; with our sons and our daughters, with our flocks and our herds we will go, for we must hold a feast to the LORD."

10 Then he said to them, "The LORD had better be with you when I let you and your little ones go! **Beware**, for **evil** is ahead of you.

11 "Not so! Go now, you who are men, and serve the LORD, for that is what you desired." And they were driven out from Pharaoh's presence.

Word Meanings:
1.   **beware:** be very careful; watch out
2.   **evil:** great danger
3.   **subtle:** something that has a sly meaning (Pharaoh pretended he did not know.)
4.   **compromise:** give up some of the demands
5.   **terms:** the conditions of an agreement

Questions:

1.   What did Pharaoh say when Moses and Aaron were brought back to him? _____

_____

2.   Then what **subtle** question did he ask them? _____

_____

3.   Whom did Moses tell him would go?

a) _____

b) _____

c) _____

4.   How did Pharaoh try to frighten Moses? _____

_____

5.   So whom would Pharaoh allow to go? _____

6.   How did Pharaoh **compromise** the **terms** that God had set? _____

_____

DAY THREE
EXODUS 10:12-20

12 Then the LORD said to Moses, "Stretch out your hand over the land of Egypt for the locusts, that they may come upon the land of Egypt, and eat every herb of the land—all that the hail has left."

13 So Moses stretched out his rod over the land of Egypt, and the LORD brought an east wind on the land all that day and all that night. When it was morning, the east wind brought the locusts.

14 And the locusts went up over all the land of Egypt and rested on all the territory of Egypt. They were very **severe; previously** there had been no such locusts as they, nor shall there be such after them.

15 For they covered the face of the whole earth, so that the land was darkened; and they ate every herb of the land and all the fruit of the trees which the hail had left. So there remained nothing green on the trees or on the plants of the field throughout all the land of Egypt.

16 Then Pharaoh called for Moses and Aaron in haste, and said, "I have sinned against the LORD your God and against you.

17 "Now therefore, please **forgive** my sin only this once, and entreat the LORD your God, that He may take away from me this death only."

18 So he went out from Pharaoh and entreated the LORD.

19 And the LORD turned a very strong west wind, which took the locusts away and blew them into the Red Sea. There remained not one locust in all the territory of Egypt.

20 But the LORD hardened Pharaoh's heart, and he did not let the children of Israel go.

Word Meanings:
1. **severe:** serious; very bad
2. **previously:** something that occurred before
3. **forgive:** to excuse for a fault or offense
4. **predicted:** to tell in advance what is going to happen
5. **extent:** the length or area which something reaches
6. **presence:** actually being in the place mentioned
7. **respect:** to pay attention to; listen to

Questions:

1. What happened that was exactly what the Lord had **predicted**? _____

_____

2. To what **extent** was the destruction? _____

3. What else was caused by the **presence** of the locusts?

    a) _____

    b) _____

4. What did Pharaoh confess to Moses? _____

_____

5. For what did he ask?

    a) _____

    b) _____

    _____

6. How did the Lord **respect** Pharaoh's wish? _____

    _____

7. Where did the locusts go? _____

8. How many locusts remained in the land of Egypt? _____

9. Did Pharaoh keep his promise to let the children of Israel go? _____

DAY FOUR
EXODUS 10:21-29

21 Then the LORD said to Moses, "Stretch out your hand toward heaven, that there may be darkness over the land of Egypt, darkness which may even be felt."

22 So Moses stretched out his hand toward heaven, and there was **thick darkness** in all the land of Egypt three days.

23 They did not see one another; nor did anyone rise from his place for three days. But all the children of Israel had light in their **dwellings**.

24 Then Pharaoh called to Moses and said, "Go, serve the LORD; only let your flocks and your herds be kept back. Let your little ones also go with you."

25 But Moses said, "You must also give us sacrifices and burnt offerings, that we may sacrifice to the LORD our God.

26 "Our livestock also shall go with us; not a hoof shall be left behind. For we must take some of them to serve the LORD our God, and even we do not know with what we must serve the LORD until we arrive there."

27 But the LORD hardened Pharaoh's heart, and he would not let them go.

28 Then Pharaoh said to him, "Get away from me! Take heed to yourself and see my face no more! For in the day you see my face you shall die!"

29 And Moses said, "You have spoken well. I will never see your face again."

Word Meanings:
1. **dwellings:** any of various types of housing where people live
2. **outcome:** result

Phrase Meaning:
    thick darkness: without even a speck of light

Questions:

1. What occurred next in the land of Egypt? _____
    _____

2. Give the results.

    a) _____

    b) _____

3. What happened in the dwellings of the children of Israel? _____

4. What compromise did Pharaoh want to make this time? _____
    _____

5. Why didn't Moses accept Pharaoh's terms? _____
    _____

6. What was the **outcome** of this meeting? _____
    _____

7. What was Pharaoh's angry command? _____

8. What did he say Moses would not see again? _____

9. What did he say would happen if he saw Moses? _____

10. How did Moses respond without anger?

    a) _____

    b) _____

DAY FIVE
EXODUS 11:1-10

1 And the LORD said to Moses, "I will bring yet one more plague on Pharaoh and on Egypt. Afterward he will let you go from here. When he lets you go, he will surely drive you out of here altogether.

2 "Speak now in the hearing of the people, and let every man ask from his neighbor and every woman from her neighbor, articles of silver and articles of gold."

3 And the LORD gave the people *favor* in the sight of the Egyptians. Moreover the man Moses was very great in the land of Egypt, in the sight of Pharaoh's servants and in the sight of the people.

4 Then Moses said, "Thus says the LORD: 'About midnight I will go out into the midst of Egypt;

5 'and all the firstborn in the land of Egypt shall die, from the firstborn of Pharaoh who sits on his throne, even to the firstborn of the female servant who is behind the handmill, and all the firstborn of the animals.

6 'Then there shall be a great cry throughout all the land of Egypt, such as was not like it before, nor shall be like it again.

7 'But **against none of the children of Israel shall a dog move its tongue**, against man or beast, that you may know that **the LORD does make a difference** between the Egyptians and Israel.'

8 "And all these your servants shall come down to me and bow down to me, saying, 'Get out, and all the people who follow you!' After that I will go out." Then he went out from Pharaoh in great anger.

9 But the LORD said to Moses, "Pharaoh will not heed you, so that My **wonders** may be multiplied in the land of Egypt."

10 So Moses and Aaron did all these wonders before Pharaoh; and the LORD hardened Pharaoh's heart, and he did not let the children of Israel go out of his land.

Word Meanings:
1. **favor:** willing to show kindness, sometimes with gifts
2. **wonders:** miracles
3. **manner:** the way of doing something
4. **regarded:** how one is thought of; respected

Phrase Meanings:
1. **against none of the children of Israel shall a dog move its tongue:** none of the Israelites would be harmed in any way
2. **the LORD does make a difference:** what affected the Egyptians would not affect the Israelites

Questions:

1. What did the Lord say He would do?_____

   _____

2. What would happen after He sent this plague? _____

   _____

3. In what **manner** would this happen? _____

4. For what were the people to ask the Egyptians? _____

   _____

5. How did the Lord accomplish this? _____

   _____

6. How was Moses **regarded** by the people and Pharaoh's servants? _____

7. When did Moses tell the people that the Lord would come into the midst of Egypt?

    _____

8. What would happen? _____

    _____

9. What would be heard throughout the land? _____

10. Did the Lord say this would ever happen again? _____

    _____

11. Would there be a difference for the children of Israel? _____

12. What message would Pharaoh send to Moses? _____

    _____

13. What reason did God give that was a result of Pharaoh not listening? _____

    _____

REVIEW
LESSON EIGHT   Exodus 10 - 11

A. True (T) or False (F): If the answer is false, write the correct answer below.

_____ 1. Pharaoh's servants said to him, "How long will this man [Moses] be a snare to us? Let the men go, that they may serve the LORD their God. Do you not yet know that Egypt is destroyed?"

_____ 2. Pharaoh said that all the people could go to worship God after the locust plague.

_____ 3. Pharaoh confessed that he had sinned against Moses and Aaron.

_____ 4. Pharaoh finally decided to let the people go after the plague of darkness.

_____ 5. About midnight, all the firstborn in the land of Egypt would die.

B. Number the ten plagues sent upon Egypt in the order in which they occurred. Then write the ten plagues in their correct order.

_____ 1. hail   1. _____

_____ 2. boils   2. _____

_____ 3. lice   3. _____

_____ 4. blood   4. _____

_____ 5. darkness   5. _____

_____ 6. locusts   6. _____

_____ 7. frogs   7. _____

_____ 8. firstborn   8. _____

_____ 9. livestock   9. _____

_____10. flies   10. _____

DISCOVERY

THE FIRST PASSOVER FEAST

DAY ONE
EXODUS 12:1-7

1 Now the LORD spoke to Moses and Aaron in the land of Egypt, saying,

2 "This month shall be your beginning of months; it shall be the first month of the year to you.

3 "Speak to all the congregation of Israel, saying: 'On the tenth day of this month every man shall take for himself a lamb, **according** to the house of his father, a lamb for a household.

4 'And if the household is too small for the lamb, let him and his neighbor next to his house take it according to the number of the persons; according to each man's need you shall make your count for the lamb.

5 'Your lamb shall be **without blemish**, a male of the first year. You may take it from the sheep or from the goats.

6 'Now you shall keep it until the fourteenth day of the same month. Then the whole assembly of the congregation of Israel shall kill it at **twilight**.

7 'And they shall take some of the blood and put it on the two doorposts and on the **lintel** of the houses where they eat it.'"

Word Meanings:
1. **according:** in the way God instructed them
2. **twilight:** the time of day between sunset and full night
3. **lintel:** the panel above the door
4. **obtain:** to choose and have ready at the time given

Phrase Meaning:
   without blemish: perfect; with no flaws

Questions:

1. What two things did the Lord tell Moses that this month would be?

   a) _____

   b) _____

2. What was the congregation of Israel to take? _____

   _____

3. What day were they to do this? _____

4. What words tell that the Lord did not want any meat wasted? _____

     _____

     _____

5. Describe the lamb they should **obtain**?

         a) _____

         b) _____

         c) _____

6. Until what day would they keep it? _____

7. When would each household in the congregation kill the lamb? _____

8. Where were they instructed to put some of the blood?

         a) _____

         b) _____

DAY TWO
EXODUS 12:8-14

8 'Then they shall eat the flesh on that night; roasted in fire, with **unleavened bread** and with **bitter herbs** they shall eat it.

9 'Do not eat it raw, nor boiled at all with water, but roasted in fire—its head with its legs and its **entrails**.

10 'You shall let none of it remain until morning, and what remains of it until morning you shall burn with fire.

11 'And thus you shall eat it: with a belt on your waist, your sandals on your feet, and your staff in your hand. So you shall eat it in **haste**. It is the LORD'S **Passover**.

12 'For I will pass through the land of Egypt on that night, and will strike all the firstborn in the land of Egypt, both man and beast; and against all the gods of Egypt I will **execute** judgment: I am the LORD.

13 'Now the blood shall be a sign for you on the houses where you are. And when I see the blood, I will pass over you; and the plague shall not be on you to destroy you when I strike the land of Egypt.

14 'So **this day shall be to you a memorial**; and you shall keep it as a feast to the LORD throughout your generations. You shall keep it as a feast by an **everlasting ordinance**.'

Word Meanings:
1. **entrails:** internal parts
2. **haste:** quickly
3. **Passover:** the night when the angel of death passed over the Israelites and they were delivered by God out of the land of Egypt
4. **execute:** to carry out; to perform what was told would be done

Phrase Meanings:
1. **unleavened bread:** bread made without yeast; it does not rise
2. **bitter herbs:** plants having a sharp, unpleasant taste
3. **this day shall be to you a memorial:** this day is a day to remember what happened
4. **everlasting ordinance:** a required ceremony to always be celebrated

Questions:

1. What would they do with the flesh of the lamb? _____

2. How was it to be prepared? _____

3. What would they also eat with the meal?

   a) _____

   b) _____

4. What three things were they instructed NOT to do?

   a) _____

   b) _____

   c) _____

5. How did God say they should eat it?

   a) _____

   b) _____

   c) _____

   d) _____

6. What was this meal called? _____

7. What was the meaning of the Passover? _____

   _____

8. What was the judgment on Egypt? _____

   _____

9. What would happen when the blood was on the Israelites' houses? _____

   _____

10. What did the Lord say this day would be?

    a) _____

    b) _____

11. How long would they keep this feast? _____

    _____

12. What did the Lord consider this feast to be? _____

    _____

DAY THREE

EXODUS 12:29-33,
40-42, 50-51

29 And it came to pass at midnight that the LORD struck all the firstborn in the land of Egypt, from the firstborn of Pharaoh who sat on his throne to the firstborn of the captive who was in the **dungeon**, and all the firstborn of livestock.

30 So Pharaoh rose in the night, he, all his servants, and all the Egyptians; and there was a great cry in Egypt, for there was not a house where there was not one dead.

31 Then he called for Moses and Aaron by night, and said, "Rise, go out from among my people, both you and the children of Israel. And go, serve the LORD as you have said.

32 "Also take your flocks and your herds, as you have said, and be gone; and bless me also."

33 And the Egyptians **urged** the people, that they might send them out of the land in haste. For they said, "We shall all be dead."

40 Now the **sojourn** of the children of Israel who lived in Egypt was four hundred and thirty years.

41 And it came to pass at the end of the four hundred and thirty years— on that very same day—it came to pass that all the armies of the LORD went out from the land of Egypt.

42 It is a night of **solemn** observance to the LORD for bringing them out of the land of Egypt. This is that night of the LORD, a solemn observance for all the children of Israel throughout their generations.

50 Thus all the children of Israel did; as the LORD commanded Moses and Aaron, so they did.

51 And it came to pass, on that very same day, that the LORD brought the children of Israel out of the land of Egypt according to their armies.

Word Meanings:
1. **dungeon:** a dark usually underground prison
2. **urged:** to strongly persuade
3. **sojourn:** a temporary stay
4. **solemn:** performed with great ceremony

Questions:

1. What came to pass at midnight? _____

   _____

2. What did Pharaoh discover when he rose in the night? _____

   _____

3. In all of Egypt, was any house spared death? _____

4. What did Pharaoh tell Moses and Aaron to do? _____

   _____

5.   Did Pharaoh give permission for all to leave as God had said? _____

6.   What were Pharaoh's last words to Moses? _____

7.   Why did the Egyptians send them out of the land in haste? _____

_____

8.   How long was the sojourn of the children of Israel in Egypt? _____

9.   What happened at the end of that time? _____

_____

10. What was this a night of? _____

11. What would always be remembered? _____

_____

12. Whom did the children of Israel listen to for this deliverance? _____

_____

13. How were the Israelites brought out of the land? _____

_____

DAY FOUR

EXODUS 13:18-19,
21-22
EXODUS 14:5-8

18 So God led the people around by way of the wilderness of the Red Sea. And the children of Israel went up in **orderly ranks** out of the land of Egypt.

19 And Moses took the bones of Joseph with him, for he had placed the children of Israel under **solemn oath**, saying, "**God will surely visit you**, and you shall carry up my bones from here with you."

21 And the LORD went before them by day in a *pillar of cloud* **to lead the way, and by night in a** *pillar of fire* **to give them light, so as to go by day and night.**

22 He did not take away the pillar of cloud by day or the pillar of fire by night from before the people.

5 Now it was told the king of Egypt that the people had fled, and the heart of Pharaoh and his servants was turned against the people; and they said, "Why have we done this, that we have let Israel go from serving us?"

6 So he made ready his **chariot** and took his people with him.

7 Also, he took six hundred choice chariots, and all the chariots of Egypt with **captains** over every one of them.

8 And the LORD hardened the heart of Pharaoh king of Egypt, and he **pursued** the children of Israel; and the children of Israel went out with **boldness.**

Word Meanings:
1. **chariot:** two-wheeled vehicle, drawn by horses
2. **captains:** those in command of groups
3. **pursued:** to follow in an effort to capture
4. **boldness:** courage; bravery
5. **prediction:** telling what will happen before the time comes
6. **regret:** to be sorry

Phrase Meanings:
1. **orderly ranks:** well-arranged groups of people
2. **solemn oath:** serious (considered sacred) promise
3. **God will surely visit you:** knowing that God would keep His promise to take them to the land He promised
4. **pillar of cloud:** a cloud for daytime observation in the shape of a pillar (tall, upright, and rounded)
5. **pillar of fire:** fire for nighttime observation in the shape of a pillar

Questions:

1. Where did God lead the people? _____

    _____

2. How did the children of Israel travel? _____

3. What did Moses take with him? _____

4. What **prediction** had been made by Joseph? _____

    _____

    _____

5. How did the Lord lead the people?

    a) _____

    b) _____

6. Did the Lord remove these signs from the people? _____

    _____

7. What was told to the king of Egypt? _____

8. Why did Pharaoh **regret** that the children of Israel had left? _____

    _____

9. What did Pharaoh decide to do? _____

10. Who and what did Pharaoh take with him? _____

    _____

11. How did the children of Israel leave? _____

DAY FIVE
EXODUS 14:10-14

10 And when Pharaoh **drew near**, the children of Israel lifted their eyes, and behold, the Egyptians marched after them. So they were very afraid, and the children of Israel cried out to the LORD.

11 Then they said to Moses, "Because there were no graves in Egypt, have you taken us away to die in the wilderness? **Why have you so dealt with us**, to bring us up out of Egypt?

12 "Is this not the word that we told you in Egypt, saying, 'Let us alone that we may serve the Egyptians'? For it would have been better for us to serve the Egyptians than that we should die in the wilderness."

13 And Moses said to the people, "Do not be afraid. Stand still, and *see the salvation of the LORD*, which He will accomplish for you today.** For the Egyptians whom you see today, you shall see again no more forever.

14 "The LORD will fight for you, and you shall *hold your peace*."

Word Meanings:
1. **accusation:** a charge of doing wrong
2. **reassuring:** taking away doubts and fears
3. **encouraging:** giving hope and support

Phrase Meanings:
1. **drew near:** came closer
2. **Why have you so dealt with us?:** Why have you done this to us?
3. **see the salvation of the Lord:** see how the Lord will rescue you
4. **hold your peace:** stop being so upset and troubled

Questions:

1. What did the children of Israel see? _____

   _____

2. What emotion did they feel? _____

3. To whom did they cry out?_____

4. Then to whom did they speak? _____

5. What **accusation** did they make? _____

   _____

6. What did they say would be better? _____

   _____

7. What **reassuring** words did Moses give the people? _____

8. What did Moses tell the people to do?

   a) _____

   b) _____

9. When would the Lord accomplish this? _____

10. What did the Lord tell Moses to say to the people about what would happen to the

    Egyptians? _____

    _____

11. What **encouraging** words did Moses give them? _____

    _____

12. What did Moses say they would do? _____

REVIEW
LESSON NINE

Exodus 12 - 14

A. Matching: Choose the correct answer and write the letter in the blank.

_____ 1. without blemish

_____ 2. share with their neighbor

_____ 3. on the two doorposts and lintel

_____ 4. a memorial to be kept as a feast

_____ 5. roasted meat, unleavened bread, and bitter herbs

_____ 6. eat in haste

_____ 7. firstborn slain

_____ 8. "Bless me also."

_____ 9. according to their armies

_____10. pillar of cloud and pillar of fire

a) Israelites left Egypt

b) God's leading

c) lamb

d) manner in which to eat

e) last plague

f) blood

g) Pharaoh

h) the Passover meal

i) the Lord's Passover

j) according to need

B. Circle the correct answer.

The children of Israel left Egypt with   a) happiness.   b) fear.   c) boldness.

C. Who spoke these words?

_____ 1. "And when I see the blood, I will pass over you; and the plague shall not be on you to destroy you when I strike the land of Egypt."

_____ 2. "Rise, go out from among my people, both you and the children of Israel."

_____ 3. "Why have you so dealt with us, to bring us up out of Egypt?"

_____ 4. "Stand still, and see the salvation of the Lord, which He will accomplish for you today."

_____ 5. "Why have we done this, that we have let Israel go from serving us?"

_____ 6. "The LORD will fight for you, and you shall hold your peace."

_____ 7. "God will surely visit you, and you shall carry up my bones from here with you."

_____ 8. "So this day shall be a memorial; and you shall keep it as a feast to the LORD throughout your generations."

Moses   Pharaoh   the Lord   Joseph   Israelites

69

DISCOVERY

MIRACLE AT THE RED SEA

MAP STUDY

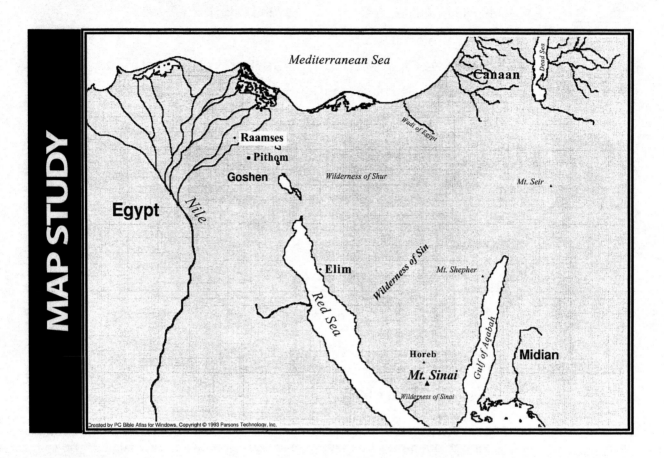

Created by PC Bible Atlas for Windows, Copyright © 1993 Parsons Technology, Inc.

Questions:

1. Draw a line where God led the people of Israel from Egypt to the Red Sea and the miracle God did there.

2. Look up this reference in your Bible: Exodus 15:27

   a) Draw some palm trees on the map to mark where the people camped before continuing their journey. Where did they camp? _____

   b) How many wells of water were there in this place?_____

   c) How many palm trees were there? _____

   d) In what area did the people camp? _____

3. Color your map (optional).

DAY ONE
EXODUS 14:15-20

> **15** And the LORD said to Moses, "Why do you cry to Me? Tell the children of Israel to go forward.
>
> **16** "But lift up your rod, and stretch out your hand over the sea and divide it. And the children of Israel shall go on dry ground through the midst of the sea.
>
> **17** "And I indeed will harden the hearts of the Egyptians, and they shall follow them. So I will gain honor over Pharaoh and over all his army, his chariots, and his horsemen.
>
> **18** "Then the Egyptians shall know that I am the LORD, when I have gained honor for Myself over Pharaoh, his chariots, and his horsemen."
>
> **19** And the Angel of God, who went before the camp of Israel, moved and went behind them; and the pillar of cloud went from before them and stood behind them.
>
> **20** So it came between the camp of the Egyptians and the camp of Israel. Thus it was a cloud and darkness to the one, and it gave light by night to the other, so that the one did not come near the other all that night.

Questions:

1. What question did the Lord ask Moses? _____

2. What positive thing did the Lord want Moses to tell the people? _____

3. What were the Lord's instructions?

    a) _____

    b) _____

    c) _____

4. What would result? _____

    _____

5. What would the Egyptians do? _____

6. What did God say would happen because of this?

    a) _____

    b) _____

7. What happened when the Angle of God and the pillar of cloud went and stood behind the camp of Israel?

    a) _____

    b) _____

    c) _____

DAY TWO
EXODUS 14:21-25

21 Then Moses stretched out his hand over the sea; and the LORD caused the sea to go back by a strong east wind all that night, and made the sea into dry land, and the waters were divided.

22 So the children of Israel went into the midst of the sea on the dry ground, and the waters were a wall to them on their right hand and on their left.

23 And the Egyptians pursued and went after them into the midst of the sea, all Pharaoh's horses, his chariots, and his horsemen.

24 Now it came to pass, in the morning watch, that the LORD looked down upon the army of the Egyptians through the pillar of fire and cloud, and He **troubled** the army of the Egyptians.

25 And He took off their chariot wheels, so that they drove them with difficulty; and the Egyptians said, "Let us **flee** from the face of Israel, for the LORD fights for them against the Egyptians."

Word Meanings:
1. **troubled:** confused and frustrated
2. **flee:** to run away from danger
3. **reaction:** how they acted because of the circumstances

Questions:

1. What did God cause to happen when Moses did as He commanded?

   a) _____

   b) _____

   c) _____

2. How did the children of Israel get across? _____

   _____

3. Where were the waters? _____

   _____

4. Where did the Egyptians pursue them? _____

5. What happened in the morning watch when the Lord looked down upon the Egyptian army?

   a) _____

   b) _____

6. What **reaction** did the Egyptians have? _____

7. Whom did they know was fighting for the Israelites? _____

DAY THREE

EXODUS 14:26-31

26 Then the LORD said to Moses, "Stretch out your hand over the sea, that the waters may come back upon the Egyptians, on their chariots, and on their horsemen."

27 And Moses stretched out his hand over the sea; and when the morning appeared, the sea returned to its full depth, while the Egyptians were fleeing into it. So the LORD **overthrew** the Egyptians in the midst of the sea.

28 Then the waters returned and covered the chariots, the horsemen, and all the army of Pharaoh that came into the sea after them. Not so much as one of them remained.

29 But the children of Israel had walked on dry land in the midst of the sea, and the waters were a wall to them on their right hand and on their left.

30 So the LORD saved Israel that day out of the hand of the Egyptians, and Israel saw the Egyptians dead on the seashore.

31 Thus Israel saw the great work which the LORD had done in Egypt; so the people feared the LORD, and believed the LORD and His servant Moses.

Word Meaning:
> **overthrew:** to bring about the downfall

Questions:

1. What did the Lord say would happen when Moses stretched his hand over the sea again?

   _____

2. What was the water's condition in the morning? _____

   _____

3. What did the Lord do? _____

   _____

4. Did any of the Egyptians remain alive? _____

5. Were the children of Israel safe? _____

6. What did Israel see?

   a) _____

   b) _____

7. Give the results of this observation of the Lord's power.

   a) _____

   b) _____

DAY FOUR
EXODUS 15:1-2, 18

> 1 Then Moses and the children of Israel sang this song to the LORD, and spoke, saying: "I will sing to the LORD, for He has triumphed gloriously! The horse and its rider He has thrown into the sea!
>
> 2 "The LORD is my strength and song, and He has become my salvation; He is my God, and I will praise Him; my father's God, and I will **exalt** Him.
>
> 18 "The LORD shall reign forever and ever."

Word Meaning:
      exalt: to give high praise

Questions:

1. What are these verses? _____

2. Who sang these words? _____

3. Give two words that describe what they are singing about. _____

4. Which three words that begin with the letter "S" express who the Lord was to them?

      a) _____

      b) _____

      c) _____

5. What were the final words of the song? _____

_____

DAY FIVE
EXODUS 15:22-27

> 22 So Moses brought Israel from the Red Sea; then they went out into the Wilderness of Shur. And they went three days in the wilderness and found no water.
>
> 23 Now when they came to Marah, they could not drink the waters of Marah, for they were bitter. Therefore the name of it was called Marah.
>
> 24 And the people complained against Moses, saying, "What shall we drink?"
>
> 25 So he cried out to the LORD, and the LORD showed him a tree. When he **cast** it into the waters, the waters were made sweet. There He made a **statute** and an **ordinance** for them. And there He tested them,
>
> 26 and said, "If you **diligently heed** the voice of the LORD your God and do what is right in His sight, **give ear** to His commandments and keep all His statutes, I will put none of the diseases on you which I have brought on the Egyptians. For I am the LORD who heals you."
>
> 27 Then they came to Elim, where there were twelve wells of water and seventy palm trees; so they camped there by the waters.

Word Meanings:
1. **cast:** to throw
2. **statute:** a law
3. **ordinance:** a decree or order
4. **diligently:** with care and effort
5. **heed:** give attention to

Phrase Meaning:
   give ear: to listen to

Questions:

1. From where did Moses bring the people?_____

2. What happened after three days in the wilderness? _____

   _____

3. Why couldn't they drink the waters in Marah? _____

4. What did the people do? _____

5. Whom did Moses cry out to? _____

6. What did the Lord do? _____

7. What happened when he cast it into the waters? _____

   _____

8. What had the Lord done in that place?

   a) _____

   b) _____

9. What did the Lord remind them to always do?

   a) _____

   b) _____

   c) _____

   d) _____

10. What would result if they did this? _____

    _____

REVIEW
LESSON TEN   Exodus 14:15 - 15:27

A. Write the correct letter(s) in the blank.

_____ 1. The Lord's instructions to Moses at the sea were
   a) "Take your shoes off before you enter the water."
   b) "Lift up your rod."
   c) "Stretch your hand over the sea."
   d) "Divide the waters."

_____ 2. The children of Israel
   a) tried to go around the water.
   b) walked across on dry land.
   c) didn't want to get wet.

_____ 3. When Moses stretched his hand over the sea again,
   a) the waters came back.
   b) there was a flood.
   c) the waters covered the Egyptians.

_____ 4. The Israelites saw and experienced
   a) the power of the Lord.
   b) their salvation.
   c) how much the Lord cared for them by saving them from the Egyptians.

_____ 5. What did the people sing about in the song to the Lord?
   a) my strength
   b) my song
   c) my son
   d) my salvation

B. Complete the following from Exodus 14:30-31.

"So the LORD saved _____ that day out of the hand of the _____, and

_____ saw the Egyptians _____ on the seashore. Thus Israel saw the great

work which the _____ had done in _____; so the people _____

the LORD, and _____ the LORD and His servant _____."

DISCOVERY

GOD PROVIDES FOR THE JOURNEY

DAY ONE
EXODUS 16:1-8

1 And they journeyed from Elim, and all the congregation of the children of Israel came to the Wilderness of Sin, which is between Elim and Sinai, on the fifteenth day of the second month after they departed from the land of Egypt.

2 Then the whole congregation of the children of Israel **complained** against Moses and Aaron in the wilderness.

3 And the children of Israel said to them, "Oh, that we had died by the hand of the LORD in the land of Egypt, when we sat by the pots of meat and when we ate bread to the full! For you have brought us out into this wilderness to kill this whole **assembly** with hunger."

4 Then the LORD said to Moses, "Behold, I will rain bread from heaven for you. And the people shall go out and gather a certain **quota** every day, that I may test them, whether they will walk in My law or not.

5 "And it shall be on the sixth day that they shall prepare what they bring in, and it shall be twice as much as they gather daily."

6 Then Moses and Aaron said to all the children of Israel, "At evening you shall know that the LORD has brought you out of the land of Egypt.

7 "And in the morning you shall see the glory of the LORD; for He hears your complaints against the LORD. But what are we, that you complain against us?"

8 Also Moses said, "This shall be seen when the LORD gives you meat to eat in the evening, and in the morning bread to the full; for the LORD hears your complaints which you make against Him. And what are we? Your complaints are not against us but against the LORD."

Word Meaning:
1. **complained:** griped; whined; protested
2. **assembly:** people gathered together
3. **quota:** an amount allowed; someone's share of something
4. **approximately:** about; nearly
5. **grievance:** complaint; protest
6. **distress:** misery
7. **portions:** parts of something
8. **accommodating:** doing something to satisfy or indulge others by giving in to their demands
9. **confirm:** to make certain; to prove

Questions:

1. **Approximately** how long had the people of Israel traveled from Egypt? _____

   _____

2. What did the people do in the wilderness? _____

   _____

3. What was the nature of their **grievance**? _____

_____

4. Whom did they blame for their **distress**? _____

5. What did the Lord tell Moses He would do? _____

6. How were the people to receive their **portions**? _____

_____

7. Give God's purpose for **accommodating** the people in this way. _____

_____

8. What was commanded for them to do on the sixth day? _____

_____

9. What did Moses say that the Lord would **confirm** to them that evening? _____

_____

10. What did God provide for them to eat in the morning? _____

11. Whom did Moses say that their complaints were against? _____

DAY TWO
EXODUS 17:1-7

1 Then all the congregation of the children of Israel set out on their journey from the Wilderness of Sin, according to the commandment of the LORD, and camped in Rephidim; but there was no water for the people to drink.

2 Therefore the people **contended** with Moses, and said, "Give us water, that we may drink." And Moses said to them, "Why do you contend with me? Why do you **tempt** the LORD?"

3 And the people thirsted there for water, and the people complained against Moses, and said, "Why is it you have brought us up out of Egypt, to kill us and our children and our livestock with thirst?"

4 So Moses cried out to the LORD, saying, "What shall I do with this people? They are almost ready to stone me!"

5 And the LORD said to Moses, "Go on before the people, and take with you some of the elders of Israel. Also take in your hand your rod with which you struck the river, and go.

6 "Behold, I will stand before you there on the rock in Horeb; and you shall strike the rock, and water will come out of it, that the people may drink." And Moses did so in the sight of the elders of Israel.

7 So he called the name of the place Massah and Meribah, because of the contention of the children of Israel, and because they tempted the LORD, saying, "Is the LORD among us or not?"

Word Meanings:
1. **contended:** argued
2. **tempt:** provoke; to irritate to the point of anger
3. **accuse:** to blame
4. **frustration:** upset; discouraged

Questions:

1. What happened at the camp of Rephidim? _____

2. What did the people do? _____

3. What did they want Moses to do? _____

_____

4. What did Moses tell them their real problem was? _____

_____

5. Of what did they **accuse** Moses? _____

_____

6. How did Moses show his **frustration** with the people? _____

_____

7. What did he think the people would do to him? _____

8. Which rod did the Lord tell Moses to take when he went before the people? _____

_____

9. What did the Lord instruct Moses to do with the rod? _____

10. What would result? _____

_____

11. What was the name of this place called? _____

12. Why was it called that? _____

_____

13. With what question had they tempted the Lord? _____

_____

DAY THREE
EXODUS 17:8-15

8 Now Amalek came and fought with Israel in Rephidim.

9 And Moses said to Joshua, "Choose us some men and go out, fight with Amalek. Tomorrow I will stand on the top of the hill with the rod of God in my hand."

10 So Joshua did as Moses said to him, and fought with Amalek. And Moses, Aaron, and Hur went up to the top of the hill.

11 And so it was, when Moses held up his hand, that Israel **prevailed**; and when he let down his hand, Amalek prevailed.

> **12** But Moses' hands became heavy; so they took a stone and put it under him, and he sat on it. And Aaron and Hur supported his hands, one on one side, and the other on the other side; and his hands were **steady** until the going down of the sun.
>
> **13** So Joshua defeated Amalek and his people with the edge of the sword.
>
> **14** Then the LORD said to Moses, "Write this for a memorial in the book and **recount** it in the hearing of Joshua, that I will utterly **blot out** the remembrance of Amalek from under heaven."
>
> **15** And Moses built an altar and called its name, The-LORD-Is-My-Banner;

Word Meanings:
1. **prevailed:** succeeded; to win
2. **steady:** firm; not shaky
3. **recount:** review and discuss what happened
4. **blot out:** to remove; to wipe out

Questions:

1 Where did Amalek come to fight with Israel? _____

2. What did Moses tell Joshua to do? _____

_____

3. What did Moses say he would do the next day? _____

4. What would he have in his hand? _____

5. Who went with Moses? _____

6. What happened when Moses held up his hand? _____

7. What occurred when he let down his hand?_____

8. What did Aaron and Hur do to prevent Moses' hands from becoming heavy?

    a) _____

    b) _____

9. How long did they do this? _____

10. Did Joshua defeat Amalek? _____

11. What did Moses then do? _____

12. What was the name given? _____

DAY FOUR
EXODUS 19:3-9

> **3** And Moses went up to God, and the LORD called to him from the mountain, saying, "Thus you shall say to the house of Jacob, and tell the children of Israel:
>
> **4** 'You have seen what I did to the Egyptians, and how **I bore you on eagles' wings** and brought you to Myself.

5 'Now therefore, if you will indeed obey My voice and keep My covenant, then you shall be a *special treasure* to Me above all people; for all the earth is Mine.

6 'And you shall be to Me a kingdom of priests and a holy nation.' These are the words which you shall speak to the children of Israel."

7 So Moses came and called for the elders of the people, and laid before them all these words which the LORD commanded him.

8 Then all the people answered together and said, "All that the LORD has spoken we will do." So Moses brought back the words of the people to the LORD.

9 And the LORD said to Moses, "Behold, I come to you in the thick cloud, that the people may hear when I speak with you, and believe you forever." So Moses told the words of the people to the LORD.

Phrase Meanings:
1. **a special treasure:** a people that are valued and cherished
2. **I bore you on eagles' wings:** I carried you to Myself to bring you to My place of safety

Questions:

1. From where did God call Moses? _____

2. To whom did God want Moses to give a message? _____

3. Of what did the Lord want Moses to remind the people ? _____

   _____

4. How did the Lord describe His care and love for them?

   a) _____

   b) _____

5. Now what did the Lord require of them?

   a) _____

   b) _____

6. What would the people be to the Lord? _____

7. What did the Lord say was His? _____

8. What else did God say He wanted the people to be?

   a) _____

   b) _____

9. What did Moses do? _____

   _____

10. How did the people respond? _____

   _____

DAY FIVE
EXODUS 19:16-20

16 Then it came to pass on the third day, in the morning, that there were thunderings and lightnings, and a thick cloud on the mountain; and the sound of the trumpet was very loud, so that all the people who were in the camp **trembled**.

17 And Moses brought the people out of the camp to meet with God, and they stood at the foot of the mountain.

18 Now Mount Sinai was completely in smoke, because the LORD **descended** upon it in fire. Its smoke **ascended** like the smoke of a furnace, and the whole mountain **quaked** greatly.

19 And when the blast of the trumpet sounded long and became louder and louder, Moses spoke, and God answered him by voice.

20 Then the LORD came down upon Mount Sinai, on the top of the mountain. And the LORD called Moses to the top of the mountain, and Moses went up.

Word Meanings:
1. **trembled:** to shake with fear
2. **descended:** came down
3. **ascended:** went up
4. **quaked:** shook violently
5. **reaction:** behavior expressed

Questions:

1. What happened on the third day?

   a) _____

   b) _____

   c) _____

2. What was the **reaction** of the people? _____

3. Where did the people stand? _____

4. What was completely in smoke? _____

5. Why? _____

6. How did the smoke ascend? _____

7. What happened to the mountain? _____

8. How did the trumpet sound? _____

9. What happened when Moses spoke? _____

10. Where did Moses go? _____

MAP STUDY

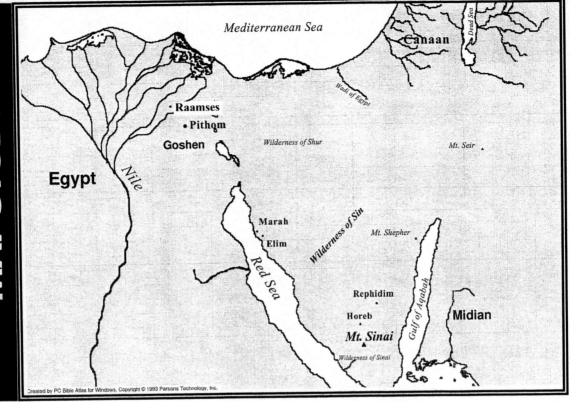

Created by PC Bible Atlas for Windows, Copyright © 1993 Parsons Technology, Inc.

Questions:

1. Look up Exodus 16:1 in your Bible.

   a) Where did the people of Israel journey from? _____
      Mark this place on your map.

   b) What does the Bible call the wilderness they were in? _____

   c) Why do you think it was called that? (Read verse 2.) _____
      _____

   d) Draw a dark cloud over this wilderness.

2. Identify Rephidim by highlighting or making an X above it.

3. Draw a black line from Egypt, to Marah, to Elim, and then to Rephidim.

4. How long had this trip from Egypt taken the children of Israel? _____

5. Look up Exodus 17:8 in your Bible.

   a) What else took place in Rephidim? _____
      _____

   b) Draw the hill where Moses stood and held his rod during the battle.

6. Look up and read Exodus 18:1-5 in your Bible. With a green pencil trace the journey that Jethro
   took as he traveled to meet Moses.

7. Draw a blue circle around Mount Sinai.

8. On a separate piece of paper, illustrate what happened at Mount Sinai. See Exodus 19:16-20.

Exodus 16 - 19

A. Write the correct letter(s) in the blank.

_____ 1. In which way(s) did the Israelites act like spoiled and pampered children?
  a) They appreciated their leader, Moses.
  b) They wanted a later bedtime.
  c) They complained about the food.

_____ 2. The word grievance means
  a) sorrow.
  b) to cry.
  c) complaint.

_____ 3. The Lord supplied food for the Israelites by
  a) telling Aaron to open a food court.
  b) raining bread from heaven.
  c) giving Moses instructions to hit a rock with his rod.

_____ 4. The Israelites had traveled from Egypt about _____ when they began to complain about lack of food.
  a) three weeks
  b) three months
  c) one month

_____ 5. The meaning of the word contended is
  a) to beg for something.
  b) argued.
  c) to provoke and irritate.

B. Complete the following from your Bible words to remember (without looking!)

"Now therefore, if you will indeed _____ My voice and keep my _____, then you shall be a special _____ to Me above all _____; for all the _____ is Mine. And you shall be to Me a _____ of _____ and a _____ nation."

C. The Lord said, "You have seen what I did to the Egyptians, and how I bore you on eagles' wings and brought you to Myself." Circle the definition that best explains the word bore.

  a) not exciting   b) to bother someone   c) carried

D. Underline what happened on Mount Sinai on the third day after the people had assembled.

  thunder   rainstorm   smoke   a thick cloud   lightning
  sound of a harp   fire   sound of a trumpet   quaking   snow

DISCOVERY

GOD'S COMMANDMENTS

DAY ONE
EXODUS 20:1-6

1 And God spoke all these words, saying:

2 "I am the LORD your God, who brought you out of the land of Egypt, out of the house of **bondage**.

3 "**You shall have no other gods before Me.**

4 "**You shall not make for yourself a carved *image***—any likeness of anything that is in heaven above, or that is in the earth beneath, or that is in the water under the earth;

5 "you shall not bow down to them nor serve them. For I, the LORD your God, am a **jealous** God, visiting the **iniquity** of the fathers on the children to the third and fourth generations of those who hate Me,

6 "but showing **mercy** to thousands, to those who love Me and keep My commandments."

Word Meanings:
1. **bondage:** slavery
2. **image:** a likeness of a god
3. **jealous:** protective of love, not wanting to share it with other gods
4. **iniquity:** sin; evil
5. **mercy:** compassion; forgiveness
6. **extent:** how much

Questions:

1. Who spoke all these words? _____

2. Who did He say He was?_____

3. What did He remind the people of? _____

   _____

4. What did He want them to remember about Egypt? _____

   _____

5. Give the first important commandment that God gave. _____

   _____

6. What should not be made? _____

7. How is this defined or explained? _____

8. To what **extent** is "anything" explained?

    a) _____

    b) _____

    c) _____

9. What did the Lord say about any other gods?

    a) _____

    b) _____

10. What reason did God give? _____

11. Compare the results of the following:

    a) those who hate the Lord _____

    _____

    b) those who follow His commandments _____

DAY TWO
EXODUS 20:7-11

7 "You shall not take the name of the LORD your God *in vain*, for the LORD will not hold him guiltless who takes His name in vain.

8 "Remember the Sabbath day, to *keep it holy*.

9 "Six days you shall labor and do all your work,

10 "but the seventh day is the Sabbath of the LORD your God. In it you shall do no work: you, nor your son, nor your daughter, nor your male servant, nor your female servant, nor your cattle, nor your stranger who is within your gates.

11 "For in six days the LORD made the heavens and the earth, the sea, and all that is in them, and rested the seventh day. Therefore the LORD blessed the Sabbath day and **hallowed** it."

Word Meaning:
1. **hallowed:** dedicated; consecrated

Phrase Meanings:
1. **in vain:** in a disrespectful way
2. **keep it [the Sabbath] holy:** to observe and honor

Questions:

1. Whose name shall not be taken in vain? _____

2. What are the consequences for one who does? _____

    _____

3. What shall you remember?_____

4. How should this day be kept? _____

5. How many days shall you labor and do your work? _____

6. What is the seventh day? _____

7. Tell what the Lord says shall not be done. _____

8. Who does God say shall not do it?

   a) _____

   b) _____

   c) _____

   d) _____

   e) _____

   f) _____

   g) _____

9. What did God accomplish in six days?

   a) _____

   _____

   b) _____

10. What reasons did God give for keeping the Sabbath day holy?

   a) _____

   _____

   b) _____

DAY THREE
EXODUS 20:12-17

12 "*Honor* your father and your mother, *that your days may be long upon the land* which the LORD your God is giving you.

13 "You shall not *murder.*

14 "You shall not commit *adultery.*

15 "You shall not *steal.*

16 "You shall not *bear false witness* against your neighbor.

17 "You shall not *covet* your neighbor's house; you shall not covet your neighbor's wife, nor his male servant, nor his female servant, nor his ox, nor his donkey, nor anything that is your neighbor's."

Word Meanings:
1. **honor:** respect
2. **murder:** taking another person's life intentionally
3. **adultery:** disloyal to the one you are married to
4. **steal:** take something that does not belong to you
5. **covet:** wanting something that someone else has
6. **relations:** involvement

Phrase Meanings:
1. **that your days may be long upon the land:** that you may live a long life
2. **bear false witness:** tell something that is untrue about someone

---

Questions:

1. Whom shall you honor? _____

2. What will result if you keep this commandment?_____
   _____

3. How many commandments are given that tell how you shall not treat others? _____

4. Write the correct commandment.

   a) Which command is against taking someone else's life? _____
   _____

   b) Which command is against having **relations** with someone you are not married to?
   _____

   c) Which command tells not to want what someone else has? _____
   _____
   _____
   _____

   d) Which command is against taking something that does not belong to you?
   _____

   e) Which command is against telling something that is not true? _____
   _____

5. How should we treat others? _____
   _____

DAY FOUR

EXODUS 20:18-22

18 Now all the people **witnessed** the thunderings, the lightning flashes, the sound of the trumpet, and the mountain smoking; and when the people saw it, they trembled and stood afar off.

19 Then they said to Moses, "You speak with us, and we will hear; but let not God speak with us, lest we die."

20 And Moses said to the people, "Do not fear; for God has come to test you, and that His fear may be before you, so that you may not sin."

21 So the people stood afar off, but Moses drew near the thick darkness where God was.

22 Then the LORD said to Moses, "Thus you shall say to the children of Israel: 'You have seen that I have talked with you from heaven.'"

Word Meaning:
witnessed: seen with one's own eyes

Questions:

1. What did the people witness?

   a) _____

   b) _____

   c) _____

   d) _____

2. What did they do when they saw it?

   a) _____

   b) _____

3. What did they ask Moses to do? _____

4. What did they say they would do? _____

5. Of whom and why were they afraid?

   a) whom: _____

   b) why: _____

6. How did Moses calm them? _____

7. What did he say was God's purpose in showing them His power?

   a) _____

   b) _____

   c) _____

8. Where did the people stand? _____

9. Where did Moses draw near? _____

10. What did the Lord tell the people? _____

    _____

DAY FIVE
EXODUS 24:12-18

12 Then the LORD said to Moses, "Come up to Me on the mountain and be there; and I will give you tablets of stone, and the law and commandments which I have written, that you may teach them."

13 So Moses arose with his assistant Joshua, and Moses went up to the mountain of God.

14 And he said to the elders, "Wait here for us until we come back to you. Indeed Aaron and Hur are with you. If any man has a difficulty, let him go to them."

15 Then Moses went up into the mountain, and a cloud covered the mountain.

16 Now the glory of the LORD rested on Mount Sinai, and the cloud covered it six days. And on the seventh day He called to Moses out of the midst of the cloud.

17 The sight of the glory of the LORD was like a consuming fire on the top of the mountain in the eyes of the children of Israel.

18 So Moses went into the midst of the cloud and went up into the mountain. And Moses was on the mountain forty days and forty nights.

Questions:

1. What did the Lord ask Moses to do? _____

_____

2. What did the Lord say He would give him? _____

3. What was written on them? _____

4. What did the Lord tell Moses to do with them? _____

5. Whom did Moses take with him? _____

6. What did he tell the elders? _____

7. Whom did he say they should go to if there was difficulty? _____

8. What covered the mountain when Moses went up? _____

9. What was on Mount Sinai? _____

10. How long did the cloud cover the mountain? _____

11. What happened on the seventh day? _____

_____

12. Who saw this sight? _____

13. How long was Moses on the mountain? _____

MAP STUDY

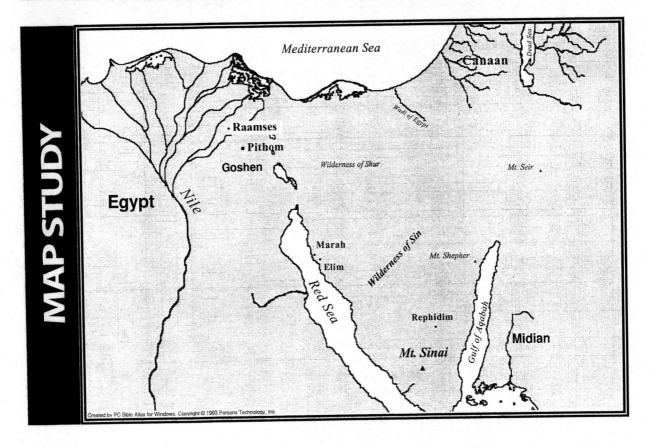

Questions:

1. Look up in your Bible: Exodus 24:12-16

    a) Identify the mountain from which the Lord spoke. _____

    b) Make a cloud over the mountain.

    c) Draw the tablets of stone near the mountain.

2. Carefully color your map with colored pencils.

REVIEW
LESSON TWELVE   Exodus 20, 24

A. Write the correct letter(s) in the blank.

_____ 1. The mountain from which God spoke and gave His commandments was
        a) Mount Horeb.
        b) Mount Ararat.
        c) Mount Sinai.

_____ 2. How does God introduce the giving of His commandments?
        a) "I am the LORD Your God."
        b) "Behold, I come to you in a thick cloud."
        c) "Whoever touches the mountain will die."

_____ 3. All the people
        a) witnessed the thunderings, the lightning, the sound of the trumpet, and the mountain smoking.
        b) fell down and worshiped the Lord.
        c) trembled and stood afar off.
        d) did not want God to speak to them because they thought they would die.

B. Complete the following commandments.

1. "You shall have no other _____ before Me."

2. "You shall not make for yourself a _____ image."

3. "You shall not take the _____ of the Lord your God in _____."

4. "Remember the _____ day, to keep it _____."

5. "Honor your _____ and your _____."

6. "You shall not _____."

7. "You shall not commit _____."

8. "You shall not _____."

9. "You shall not bear _____ witness against your _____."

10. "You shall not _____ anything that is your _____."

C. Summary

1. How many commandments are about people's responsibility toward God? _____

2. How many commandments are about how we should treat others? _____

DISCOVERY

GOD'S INSTRUCTIONS FOR THE TABERNACLE

DAY ONE
EXODUS 25:1-9

1 Then the LORD spoke to Moses, saying:

2 "Speak to the children of Israel, that they bring Me an offering. From everyone who gives it **willingly** with his heart you shall take My offering.

3 "And this is the offering which you shall take from them: gold, silver, and bronze;

4 "blue, purple, and **scarlet** thread, fine **linen**, and goats' hair;

5 "ram skins dyed red, badger skins, and **acacia** wood;

6 "oil for the light, and spices for the anointing oil and for the sweet **incense**;

7 "onyx stones, and stones to be set in the **ephod** and in the **breastplate**.

8 "And let them make Me a **sanctuary**, that I may **dwell** among them.

9 "According to all that I show you, that is, the pattern of the **tabernacle** and the pattern of all its **furnishings**, just so you shall make it."

Word Meanings:
1. **willingly:** to volunteer; done without forcing
2. **scarlet:** bright red
3. **linen:** cloth made from flax (a plant)
4. **acacia:** a type of tree that grows in warm regions
5. **incense:** a spice being burned to create a sweet smell
6. **ephod:** a linen garment worn by the high priest
7. **breastplate:** a square piece of cloth upon which twelve precious stones were set in gold. It was fastened to the ephod and worn over the high priest's heart.
8. **sanctuary:** a holy place where the ark of the Testimony (see page 94) was placed
9. **dwell:** to live
10. **tabernacle:** the sacred tent for worship that could be moved
11. **furnishings:** pieces of furniture

Questions:
1. What did the Lord tell Moses to ask the children of Israel to bring? _____
2. How should it be given? _____
3. What precious metals were given? _____
4. Give the colors of the thread. _____
5. Which material is mentioned? _____
6. Name the skins offered. _____

7. Give the reason for the oil. _____

8. For what were the spices to be used? _____

_____

9. Where were the onyx stones to be set? _____

_____

10. For what purpose was the sanctuary? _____

_____

11. How would the people know how to make the tabernacle? _____

_____

12. For what else would God give instructions? _____

_____

DAY TWO

EXODUS 25:10-11,
16-19, 21-22

> **10** "And they shall make an ark of acacia wood; two and a half cubits shall be its length, a **cubit** and a half its width, and a cubit and a half its height.
>
> **11** "And you shall overlay it with pure gold, inside and out you shall overlay it, and shall make on it a **molding** of gold all around.
>
> **16** "And you shall put into the **ark the Testimony** which I will give you.
>
> **17** "You shall make a **mercy seat** of pure gold; two and a half cubits shall be its length and a cubit and a half its width.
>
> **18** "And you shall make two **cherubim** of gold; of hammered work you shall make them at the two ends of the mercy seat.
>
> **19** "Make one cherub at one end, and the other cherub at the other end; you shall make the cherubim at the two ends of it of one piece with the mercy seat.
>
> **21** "You shall put the mercy seat on top of the ark, and in the ark you shall put **the Testimony** that I will give you.
>
> **22** "And there I will meet with you, and I will speak with you from above the mercy seat, from between the two cherubim which are on the ark of the Testimony, about everything which I will give you in commandment to the children of Israel."

Word Meanings:
1. **cubit:** a measure of length of about 18 inches
2. **molding:** a strip for decorating a surface
3. **ark of the Testimony:** gold covered chest which contained the Ten Commandments, a golden pot of manna and Aaron's rod that budded
4. **mercy seat:** the lid for the ark of the Testimony
5. **cherubim:** winged creatures (plural of cherub)
6. **the Testimony:** the two tablets of the Ten Commandments

Questions:

1.　Of what would the ark be made? _____

2.　What would the overlay be? _____

3.　What was to be made of pure gold? _____

4.　Where were the two cherubim of gold to be placed? _____

5.　What was to be placed on top of the ark? _____

6.　What was to be placed into the ark? _____

7.　What would happen above the mercy seat, between the two cherubim? _____
_____

DAY THREE

EXODUS 27:21
EXODUS 28:1-4

---

21 "In the tabernacle of meeting, outside the **veil** which is before the Testimony, Aaron and his sons shall **tend** it from evening until morning before the LORD. It shall be a **statute** forever to their generations on behalf of the children of Israel.

1 "Now take Aaron your brother, and his sons with him, from among the children of Israel, that he may minister to Me as **priest**, Aaron and Aaron's sons: Nadab, Abihu, Eleazar, and Ithamar.

2 "And you shall make holy garments for Aaron your brother, for glory and for beauty.

3 "So you shall speak to all who are gifted **artisans**, whom I have filled with the spirit of wisdom, that they may make Aaron's garments, to **consecrate** him, that he may minister to Me as priest.

4 "And these are the garments which they shall make: a breastplate, an ephod, a robe, a skillfully woven **tunic**, a **turban**, and a **sash**. So they shall make holy garments for Aaron your brother and his sons, that he may minister to Me as priest."

Word Meanings:

1.　**veil:** a woven divider between the holy place and the Most Holy
2.　**tend:** take care of
3.　**statute:** a law
4.　**priest:** one who prays for the people and ministers to the Lord
5.　**artisans:** those who are extremely skilled and talented in a craft
6.　**consecrate:** to set apart as holy
7.　**tunic:** a loose-fitting garment usually knee-length or longer
8.　**turban:** a covering for the head
9.　**sash:** a band worn around the waist

Questions:

1.　Who would tend the tabernacle? _____

2.　What was the time of tending? _____

3. a) The instructions for tending the tabernacle the Lord gave to Moses shall be a _____.

    b) For how long and to whom would this be? _____

    _____

4. Who was to be the Lord's priest? _____

5. What were the names of Aaron's sons? _____

    _____

6. What would the priest wear? _____

7. For what purpose? _____

8. To whom would Moses speak? _____

9. Who had filled them with the spirit of wisdom? _____

10. What were they to do? _____

11. List what Aaron would wear when he ministered to the Lord.

    a) _____

    b) _____

    c) _____

    d) _____

    e) _____

    f) _____

DAY FOUR

EXODUS 28:29
EXODUS 29:4-9

29 "So Aaron shall bear the names of the sons of Israel on the breastplate of judgment over his heart, when he goes into the holy place, as a **memorial** before the LORD continually.

4 "And Aaron and his sons you shall bring to the door of the tabernacle of meeting, and you shall wash them with water.

5 "Then you shall take the garments, put the tunic on Aaron, and the robe of the ephod, the ephod, and the breastplate, and **gird** him with the **intricately** woven band of the ephod.

6 "You shall put the turban on his head, and put the holy crown on the turban.

7 "And you shall take the **anointing oil**, pour it on his head, and **anoint** him.

8 "Then you shall bring his sons and put tunics on them.

9 "And you shall gird them with sashes, Aaron and his sons, and put the hats on them. The priesthood shall be theirs for a **perpetual** statute. So you shall consecrate Aaron and his sons."

Word Meanings:
1. **memorial:** remembrance
2. **gird:** to encircle or fasten with a belt or band
3. **intricately:** skillfully
4. **anointing oil:** a special blend of oils and spices that was used to anoint the tabernacle, its furnishings, and the priests
5. **anoint:** to consecrate; to pour oil upon in a ceremony
6. **perpetual:** not stopping; lasting a long time

Questions:

1. What would Aaron do? _____

2. Where were these placed? _____
   _____

3. When would this be worn?_____
   _____

4. What reason did the Lord give? _____
   _____

5. Who was to be brought to the door of the tabernacle of meeting? _____

6. What was to be done to them there? _____

7. What garments were put on Aaron?

   a) _____

   b) _____

   c) _____

   d) _____

   e) _____

8. What was put on his head? _____

9. How was Moses to anoint Aaron? _____

10. What was put on Aaron's sons?

    a) _____

    b) _____

    c) _____

11. What was to be a perpetual statute for them? _____

12. Moses would _____ Aaron and his sons by doing these things that
    the Lord commanded.

DAY FIVE

EXODUS 29:38-39, 42-46

38 "Now this is what you shall offer on the altar: two lambs of the first year, day by day continually.

39 "One lamb you shall offer in the morning, and the other lamb you shall offer at twilight.

42 "This shall be a continual burnt offering throughout your generations at the door of the tabernacle of meeting before the LORD, where I will meet you to speak with you.

43 "And there I will meet with the children of Israel, and the tabernacle shall be sanctified by My glory.

44 "So I will consecrate the tabernacle of meeting and the altar. I will also consecrate both Aaron and his sons to minister to Me as priests.

45 "I will dwell among the children of Israel and will be their God.

46 "And they shall know that I am the LORD their God, who brought them up out of the land of Egypt, that I may dwell among them. I am the LORD their God."

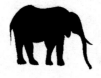

Questions:

1. The Lord gave instructions for what to be offered on the altar? _____

_____

2. How often would they do this? _____

3. When would the offering be made?

    a) _____

    b) _____

4. For how long would the burnt offering be continued? _____

_____

5. Where would the Lord meet His people to speak to them? _____

_____

6. How would the tabernacle be sanctified (set apart for a sacred purpose)? _____

_____

7. What and whom did the Lord say He would consecrate?

    a) _____

    b) _____

    c) _____

8. With whom would the Lord dwell? _____

9. What did He say He would be? _____

10. What did He say they shall know? _____

11. From where had He brought them? _____

12. What was His purpose? _____

13. Whom did He say He was? _____

REVIEW
LESSON
THIRTEEN

Exodus 25 - 29

A. Write the correct letter(s) in the blank.

_____ 1. With what attitude were the people to bring an offering?
        a) with fear
        b) with sad hearts
        c) with willing hearts

_____ 2. The purpose of the sanctuary was
        a) to listen to a priest.
        b) a place to bring their offering.
        c) to bring the sacrifice.
        d) so the Lord could dwell among His people.

_____ 3. Which of the following would Moses do to Aaron and his sons?
        a) anoint them
        b) give them an offering
        c) consecrate them
        d) wash them with water

_____ 4. How long would the burnt offering be continued?
        a) only on the Sabbath
        b) only during times of worship
        c) day by day continually

_____ 5. How would the tabernacle be sanctified?
        a) by God's glory
        b) by the sacrifices that were offered
        c) by the incense on the altar

B. True (T) or False (F): If the answer is false, write the correct answer below.

_____ 1. The people's offering to the Lord was used to make the sanctuary and it's furnishings.

_____ 2. The instructions for the tabernacle were given by Moses.

_____ 3. The name of the sons of Israel would be worn by Aaron when He went into the holy place.

_____ 4. Aaron wore holy garments made by gifted artisans.

_____ 5. The burnt offering would be made in the morning, at noon, and in the evening.

C. Bonus!

What did the Lord say He wanted His people to know? _____

_____

DISCOVERY

GOD'S INSTRUCTION FOR WORSHIP

DAY ONE
EXODUS 30:11-16

11 Then the LORD spoke to Moses, saying:

12 "When you take the **census** of the children of Israel for their number, then every man shall give a **ransom** for himself to the LORD, when you number them, that there may be no **plague** among them when you number them.

13 "This is what everyone among those who are numbered shall give: half a **shekel** according to the shekel of the sanctuary (a shekel is twenty gerahs). The half-shekel shall be an offering to the LORD.

14 "Everyone included among those who are numbered, from twenty years old and above, shall give an offering to the LORD.

15 "The rich shall not give more and the poor shall not give less than half a shekel, when you give an offering to the LORD, to make **atonement** for yourselves.

16 "And you shall take the atonement money of the children of Israel, and shall appoint it for the service of the tabernacle of meeting, that it may be a memorial for the children of Israel before the LORD, to make atonement for yourselves."

Word Meanings:
1. **census:** a counting of the people
2. **ransom:** payment
3. **plague:** a terrible disaster
4. **shekel:** a coin; money
5. **atonement:** payment for sin

Questions:

1. What did the Lord tell Moses to take? _____

    _____

2. What would every man do? _____

    _____

3. Why was it important for them to do this when Moses numbered them? _____

    _____

4. What was each one numbered to give? _____

5. What was the purpose of this? _____

    _____

6. Who would be instructed to give? _____

    _____

7. What should the rich give?_____

8. What should the poor give? _____

9. Why was this offering given? _____

10. For what would the offering be used? _____

_____

DAY TWO

EXODUS 31:1-7

> **1** Then the LORD spoke to Moses, saying:
>
> **2** "See, I have called by name Bezalel the son of Uri, the son of Hur, of the tribe of Judah.
>
> **3** "And I have filled him with the Spirit of God, in wisdom, in understanding, in knowledge, and in all manner of workmanship,
>
> **4** "to design artistic works, to work in gold, in silver, in bronze,
>
> **5** "in cutting jewels for setting, in carving wood, and to work in all manner of workmanship.
>
> **6** "And I, indeed I, have appointed with him Aholiab the son of Ahisamach, of the tribe of Dan; and I have put wisdom in the hearts of all who are gifted artisans, that they may make all that I have commanded you:
>
> **7** "the tabernacle of meeting, the ark of the Testimony and the mercy seat that is on it, and all the furniture of the tabernacle."

Questions:

1. Whom did the Lord tell Moses He had called for special workmanship? _____

2. Which tribe was this man from? _____

3. What had the Lord filled him with? _____

4. What four things would he be given through this?

   a) _____ c) _____

   b) _____ d) _____

5. For what purpose would these gifts be useful?

   a) _____

   b) _____

   c) _____

   d) _____

   e) _____

6. Whom did the Lord also appoint? _____

7. What special things would these men make?

   a) _____

   b) _____

   c) _____

   d) _____

DAY THREE
EXODUS 31:12-18

12 And the LORD spoke to Moses, saying,

13 "Speak also to the children of Israel, saying: 'Surely My Sabbaths you shall keep, for it is a sign between Me and you throughout your generations, that you may know that I am the LORD who **sanctifies** you.

14 'You shall keep the Sabbath, therefore, for it is holy to you. Everyone who **profanes** it shall surely be put to death; for whoever does any work on it, that person shall be cut off from among his people.

15 'Work shall be done for six days, but the seventh is the Sabbath of rest, holy to the LORD. Whoever does any work on the Sabbath day, he shall surely be put to death.

16 'Therefore the children of Israel shall keep the Sabbath, to observe the Sabbath throughout their generations as a *perpetual covenant*.

17 'It is a sign between Me and the children of Israel forever; for in six days the LORD made the heavens and the earth, and on the seventh day He rested and was *refreshed*.'"

18 And when He had made an end of speaking with him on Mount Sinai, He gave Moses two **tablets** of the Testimony, tablets of stone, written with the finger of God.

Word Meanings:
1. **sanctifies:** frees from sin; purifies
2. **profanes:** dishonors; to be irreverent
3. **perpetual:** endless; lasting; permanent
4. **covenant:** a binding agreement
5. **refreshed:** to receive new strength
6. **tablets:** flat stones for writing

Questions:

1. What did the Lord tell Moses to remind the children of Israel? _____
   _____

2. What did the Lord want them to know by doing this?_____
   _____

3. What would happen to those who would profane it? _____

4. What were the consequences for those who would work on the Sabbath? _____
   _____

5. How many days are given to work? _____

6. For what purpose is the Sabbath?
   a) _____
   b) _____

7. When would this sign of the covenant end?_____

8. What had the Lord given as an example of this in the beginning?

    a) _____

        _____

    b) _____

        _____

9. Where was the Lord speaking these words? _____

10. What did He give Moses when He was finished speaking? _____

    _____

11. What were they made of? _____

12. How were these tablets written? _____

DAY FOUR
EXODUS 32:1-6

1 Now when the people saw that Moses **delayed** coming down from the mountain, the people gathered together to Aaron, and said to him, "Come, make us gods that shall go before us; for as for this Moses, the man who brought us up out of the land of Egypt, we do not know what has become of him."

2 And Aaron said to them, "Break off the golden earrings which are in the ears of your wives, your sons, and your daughters, and bring them to me."

3 So all the people broke off the golden earrings which were in their ears, and brought them to Aaron.

4 And he received the gold from their hand, and he **fashioned** it with an **engraving** tool, and made a **molded** calf. Then they said, "This is your god, O Israel, that brought you out of the land of Egypt!"

5 So when Aaron saw it, he built an altar before it. And Aaron made a **proclamation** and said, "Tomorrow is a feast to the LORD."

6 Then they rose early on the next day, offered burnt offerings, and brought peace offerings; and the people sat down to eat and drink, and rose up to play.

Word Meanings:
1. **delayed:** was slow
2. **fashioned:** formed; created with materials available
3. **engraving:** carving
4. **molded:** shaped in the form of something
5. **proclamation:** announcement
6. **comply:** agree to

Questions:

1. Why were the people impatient? _____

_____

2. What did they do when they got tired of waiting? _____

_____

3. What did they ask him to do? _____

_____

4. What did they say about Moses?

    a) _____

_____

    b) _____

_____

5. How did Aaron **comply** with their request? _____

_____

6. What did Aaron do with the gold? _____

_____

7. What did he say to them about this god? _____

_____

8. What else did Aaron do? _____

9. What proclamation did he make? _____

10. What did the people do early the next day?

    a) _____

    b) _____

    c) _____

    d) _____

DAY FIVE
EXODUS 32:7-10

7 And the LORD said to Moses, "Go, get down! For your people whom you brought out of the land of Egypt have **corrupted** themselves.

8 "They have turned aside quickly out of the way which I commanded them. They have made themselves a molded calf, and worshiped it and sacrificed to it, and said, 'This is your god, O Israel, that brought you out of the land of Egypt!'"

9 And the LORD said to Moses, "I have seen this people, and indeed it is a **stiff-necked people**!

10 "Now therefore, let Me alone, that **My wrath may burn hot** against them and I may **consume** them. And I will make of you a great nation."

Word Meanings:
1. **corrupted:** to become wicked
2. **consume:** to destroy

Phrase Meanings:
1. **stiff-necked people:** a stubborn and rebellious people
2. **My wrath may burn hot:** My anger will burst in flames to destroy

Questions:

1. What command did the Lord give Moses? _____

2. Why was the command given? _____

_____

3. From what did the Lord say they had turned aside quickly? _____

_____

4. What awful thing had they done? _____

_____

5. What did they do with what they made? _____

_____

6. What god did they say had brought them out of the land of Egypt? _____

7. What did the Lord say about the people? _____

_____

8. Why did the Lord say to Moses, "Let Me alone"?

   a) _____

   b) _____

9. What did the Lord say about Moses? _____

_____

REVIEW
LESSON
FOURTEEN

Exodus 30:11 - 32:10

A. Matching: Write the correct letter in the blank.

_____ 1. sanctifies   a) not stopping; lasting a long time

_____ 2. ransom   b) dishonors; to be irreverent

_____ 3. profanes   c) frees from sin; purifies

_____ 4. perpetual   d) a binding agreement

_____ 5. covenant   e) payment

B. Phrase Meaning: Tell who said these words and put the phrase in your own words.

"It is a stiff-necked people!" _____

_____

C. Write the correct letter(s) in the blank.

_____ 1. Who was to give the greatest offering for atonement?
           a) the people over twenty years old
           b) the workers
           c) the poor
           d) the rich
           e) they would all give the same amount

_____ 2. What did God give the man chosen for special workmanship?
           a) jewels
           b) wisdom
           c) gold and silver
           d) understanding
           e) knowledge

D. True (T) or False (F): If the answer is false, write the correct answer below.

_____ 1. The purpose of the Sabbath is for rest and worship.

_____ 2. The people were impatient because Moses delayed coming down from the mountain.

_____ 3. Moses wrote on the tablets what God had told him.

 # DISCOVERY

A DIFFICULT PEOPLE

DAY ONE
EXODUS 32:11-14

11 Then Moses **pleaded** with the LORD his God, and said: "LORD, why does Your wrath burn hot against Your people whom You have brought out of the land of Egypt with great power and with a mighty hand?

12 "Why should the Egyptians speak, and say, 'He brought them out to harm them, to kill them in the mountains, and to consume them from the face of the earth'? Turn from Your fierce wrath, and **relent** from this harm to Your people.

13 "Remember Abraham, Isaac, and Israel, Your servants, to whom You **swore** by Your own self, and said to them, 'I will multiply your descendants as the stars of heaven; and all this land that I have spoken of I give to your descendants, and they shall inherit it forever.'"

14 So the LORD relented from the harm which He said He would do to His people.

Word Meanings:
1. **pleaded:** begged
2. **relent:** to become less severe

3. **swore:** promised

Questions:

1. What did Moses do? _____

2. What question did He ask? _____
   _____

3. What did he remind the Lord? _____
   _____

4. How did he say that God had done this? _____
   _____

5. What did Moses say that the Egyptians would think if God used His wrath on these people?

   a) _____

   b) _____

   c) _____

6. What did Moses ask God to do?

   a) _____

   b) _____

7. Whom did he ask God to remember? _____

8. What promise did Moses remind God He had sworn?

   a) _____

   _____

   b) _____

   _____

   c) _____

9. What words tell us that the Lord listened to Moses and his concern for the people?

   _____

   _____

DAY TWO
EXODUS 32:15-18

15 And Moses turned and went down from the mountain, and the two tablets of the Testimony were in his hand. The tablets were written on both sides; on the one side and on the other they were written.

16 Now the tablets were the work of God, and the writing was the writing of God **engraved** on the tablets.

17 And when Joshua heard the noise of the people as they shouted, he said to Moses, "There is a noise of war in the camp."

18 But he said: "It is not the noise of the shout of **victory**, Nor the noise of the cry of **defeat**, but the sound of singing I hear."

Word Meanings:
1. **engraved:** carved, cut, or etched into a material
2. **victory:** the overcoming of an enemy; winning a battle
3. **defeat:** the loss of a contest or battle

Questions:

1. What did Moses do? _____

2. What were in his hand? _____

3. Where was the writing on the tablets? _____

4. Whose work was on the tablets? _____

5. How was the writing produced? _____

6. What did Joshua think when he heard the noise of the people as they shouted?

   _____

7. What did Moses say the noise was not about?

   a) _____

   b) _____

8. What could he hear? _____

DAY THREE
EXODUS 32:19-24

19 So it was, as soon as he came near the camp, that he saw the calf and the dancing. So Moses' anger became hot, and he **cast** the tablets out of his hands and broke them at the foot of the mountain.

20 Then he took the calf which they had made, burned it in the fire, and ground it to powder; and he scattered it on the water and made the children of Israel drink it.

21 And Moses said to Aaron, "What did this people do to you that you have brought so great a sin upon them?"

22 So Aaron said, "Do not let the anger of my lord become hot. You know the people, that they are set on evil.

23 "For they said to me, 'Make us gods that shall go before us; as for this Moses, the man who brought us out of the land of Egypt, we do not know what has become of him.'

24 "And I said to them, 'Whoever has any gold, let them break it off.' So they gave it to me, and I cast it into the fire, and this calf came out."

Word Meanings:
1. **cast:** threw down
2. **reprimand:** to speak strongly to because of a wrongdoing
3. **excuse:** reason given to remove the blame
4. **explanation:** a reason

Questions:

1. What two things did Moses see as he came near the camp?

   a) _____

   b) _____

2. What emotion did Moses feel? _____

3. What did he do? _____

4. What happened? _____

5. What four things did Moses do with the golden calf they had made?

   a) _____

   b) _____

   c) _____

   d) _____

6. What **reprimand** did Moses give to Aaron in making him responsible for allowing this?

   _____

   _____

7. What was Aaron's response? _____

   _____

8. What **excuse** did he make to put the blame back on the people? _____

    _____

9. What **explanation** did Aaron give to Moses that was not true? _____

    _____

10. Compare Aaron's answer to what really happened. _____

    _____

    _____

DAY FOUR

EXODUS 32:25-26, 29

> **25** Now when Moses saw that the people were **unrestrained** (for Aaron had not restrained them, to their **shame** among their enemies),
>
> **26** then Moses stood in the entrance of the camp, and said, "Whoever is on the LORD's side—come to me!" And all the sons of Levi gathered themselves together to him.
>
> **29** Then Moses said, "**Consecrate** yourselves today to the LORD, that He may **bestow** on you a blessing this day, for every man has **opposed** his son and his brother."

Word Meanings:
1. **unrestrained:** not controlled
2. **shame:** to be embarrassed by an action
3. **consecrate:** to set apart for God's use
4. **bestow:** to give or present
5. **opposed:** acted against
6. **accountable:** responsible; required to give an explanation

Questions:

1. What had Moses observed? _____

2. Whom did he hold **accountable** for this? _____

3. Among whom would they receive shame for this behavior? _____

4. What did Moses tell them in the entrance of the camp? _____

    _____

5. Who gathered themselves together to him? _____

6. What did Moses tell the people they must do then? _____

    _____

7. What would the Lord do? _____

8. Why would they receive this?_____

    _____

DAY FIVE
EXODUS 32:30-35

> **30** Now it came to pass on the next day that Moses said to the people, "You have committed a great sin. So now I will go up to the LORD; perhaps I can make atonement for your sin."
>
> **31** Then Moses returned to the LORD and said, "Oh, these people have committed a great sin, and have made for themselves a god of gold!
>
> **32** "Yet now, if You will forgive their sin—but if not, I pray, **blot** me **out of Your book** which You have written."
>
> **33** And the LORD said to Moses, "Whoever has sinned against Me, I will blot him out of My book.
>
> **34** "Now therefore, go, lead the people to the place of which I have spoken to you. Behold, My Angel shall go before you. Nevertheless, in the day when I visit for punishment, I will visit punishment upon them for their sin."
>
> **35** So the LORD plagued the people because of what they did with the calf which Aaron made.

Phrase Meaning:
> **blot out of Your book:** erase the names of those who reject God

Questions:

1. What did Moses remind the people they had done? _____

_____

2. What did Moses say he would do for them? _____

3. What was his purpose? _____

4. What did Moses say when he returned to the Lord? _____

_____

5. How did he plead for the people to the Lord? _____

6. If the Lord could not do what he asked, what did Moses say should happen to him?

_____

7. What did the Lord say about those who had sinned? _____

_____

8. Did the Lord think that Moses had sinned? _____

9. What did the Lord tell Moses to do? _____

_____

10. Who would go before Moses? _____

11. What did the Lord say would happen in the day He visited? _____

_____

12. What did the Lord do? _____

_____

MEMORY

PSALM 37:23-24

23 The steps of a good man are ordered by the LORD, and He delights in his way.

24 Though he fall, he shall not be utterly cast down; for the LORD upholds him with His hand.

REVIEW
LESSON
FIFTEEN

Exodus 32

A. Write the correct letter(s) in the blank.

_____ 1. Moses showed his love for the people of Israel by
   a) asking God to change His mind about destroying them.
   b) waiting for a few days to see if the people would repent.
   c) reminding God of the promise He had given to His servants.

_____ 2. What did Moses bring down from the mountain with him?
   a) his rod
   b) a scroll with the Ten Commandments written on it
   c) two tablets of the Testimony

_____ 3. When Moses came near the camp, what did he hear and see?
   a) the molded calf
   b) the people dancing
   c) the sound of singing
   d) the people preparing for war

B. Connect the speaker with these words and write the correct name in the blank.

_____ 1. "Do not let the anger of my lord become hot."

_____ 2. "Whoever is on the LORD's side—come to me!"

_____ 3. "There is a noise of war in the camp."

_____ 4. "Make us gods that shall go out before us."

_____ 5. "Whoever has sinned against Me, I will blot him out of My book."

　　　God　　　　　Joshua　　　　Moses　　　　Aaron　　　Israelites

C. Challenge: Short answer.

1. Tell what you can learn from the study this week that the Israelites had to learn.

_____

_____

_____

_____

2. What do you think Moses learned from the events in this chapter?

_____

_____

_____

_____

DISCOVERY

GOD'S GUIDANCE FOR HIS PEOPLE

DAY ONE
EXODUS 33:12-16

12 Then Moses said to the LORD, "See, You say to me, 'Bring up this people.' But You have not let me know whom You will send with me. Yet You have said, 'I know you by name, and you have also found **grace** in My sight.'

13 "Now therefore, I pray, if I have found grace in Your sight, show me now Your way, that I may know You and that I may find grace in Your sight. And **consider** that this nation is Your people."

14 And He said, "My Presence will go with you, and I will give you rest."

15 Then he said to Him, "If Your Presence does not go with us, do not bring us up from here.

16 "For how then will it be known that Your people and I have found grace in Your sight, except You go with us? So we shall be **separate**, Your people and I, from all the people who are upon the face of the earth."

Word Meanings:
1. **grace:** favor
2. **consider:** to think about and remember
3. **separate:** different and distinct
4. **concern:** something someone seriously cares about
5. **mission:** sent for a special purpose
6. **confidence:** to be sure and secure in what is known
7. **assurance:** a promise that is made more certain

Questions:

1. What did Moses say to the Lord that showed **concern** for his **mission**? _____

   _____

2. What had the Lord told Moses that gave him **confidence**?

   a) _____

   b) _____

3. What other **assurance** did Moses ask for? _____

   _____

4. What did Moses ask the Lord to do for the people? _____

   _____

5. What two things did the Lord promise Moses?

   a) _____

   b) _____

6.　With what words did Moses respond? _____

_____

7.　What did Moses say these people would be upon the face of the earth? _____

_____

DAY TWO
EXODUS 33:17-23

17 So the LORD said to Moses, "I will also do this thing that you have spoken; for you have found grace in My sight, and I know you by name."

18 And he said, "Please, show me Your glory."

19 Then He said, "I will make all My goodness pass before you, and I will **proclaim** the name of the LORD before you. I will be **gracious** to whom I will be gracious, and I will have **compassion** on whom I will have compassion."

20 But He said, "You cannot see My face; for no man shall see Me, and live."

21 And the LORD said, "Here is a place by Me, and you shall stand on the rock.

22 "So it shall be, while My glory passes by, that I will put you in the **cleft of the rock**, and will cover you with My hand while I pass by.

23 "Then I will take away My hand, and you shall see My back; but My face shall not be seen."

Word Meanings:
1. **proclaim:** to make something known
2. **gracious:** kind and forgiving
3. **compassion:** pity or sympathy and the desire to help

Phrase Meaning:
cleft of the rock: a crack or a split in the rock

Questions:

1.　What did the Lord agree to do? _____

2.　What did God say to Moses?

　　　a) _____

　　　b) _____

3.　What is added to Moses' request to the Lord? _____

4.　How did the Lord say He would do this? (Give the four "I will's.")

　　　a) _____

　　　b) _____

c) _____

d) _____

_____

5. Why did the Lord say Moses could not see His face? _____

_____

6. Where did the Lord say there was a place? _____

7. What did the Lord instruct Moses to do? _____

8. What would pass by Moses? _____

9. Then what did the Lord say He would do? (Give two "I will's.")

a) _____

b) _____

10. What would happen when the Lord took away His hand? _____

_____

DAY THREE
EXODUS 34:1, 4-9

1 And the LORD said to Moses, "Cut two tablets of stone like the first ones, and I will write on these tablets the words that were on the first tablets which you broke."

4 So he cut two tablets of stone like the first ones. Then Moses rose early in the morning and went up Mount Sinai, as the LORD had commanded him; and he took in his hand the two tablets of stone.

5 Now the LORD descended in the cloud and stood with him there, and proclaimed the name of the LORD.

6 And the LORD passed before him and proclaimed, "The LORD, the LORD God, merciful and gracious, **longsuffering**, and **abounding** in goodness and truth,

7 "keeping mercy for thousands, forgiving **iniquity** and **transgression** and **sin**, by no means clearing the guilty, visiting the iniquity of the fathers upon the children and the children's children to the third and the fourth generation."

8 So Moses made haste and bowed his head toward the earth, and worshiped.

9 Then he said, "If now I have found grace in Your sight, O Lord, let my Lord, I pray, go among us, even though we are a stiff-necked people; and **pardon** our iniquity and our sin, and take us as Your **inheritance**."

Word Meanings:
1. **longsuffering:** patiently bearing wrongs
2. **abounding:** to have a great amount
3. **iniquity:** wickedness
4. **transgression:** action which is against the law
5. **sin:** disobedience and rebellion against God
6. **pardon:** to forgive
7. **inheritance:** possession

Questions:

1. What was the Lord's instruction to Moses? _____

2. What would they be like? _____

    _____

3. What would the Lord do? _____

    _____

4. Where did Moses take the new tablets? _____

5. When did he leave to go there? _____

6. Into what did the Lord descend? _____

7. Where did the Lord stand? _____

8. What did He proclaim about the Lord God?

    a) _____

    b) _____

    c) _____

    d) _____

    e) _____

9. What were the consequences for those who were guilty? (**Note:** The guilty are those who do

    not ask for God's forgiveness and are not sorry for their sins.) _____

    _____

10. What did Moses do in haste?

    a) _____

    b) _____

11. What was Moses' request if he had found grace in the Lord's sight and even though they

    were a stiff-necked people?

    a) _____

    b) _____

    c) _____

DAY FOUR
EXODUS 34:27-32

27 Then the LORD said to Moses, "Write these words, for according to the **tenor** of these words I have made a covenant with you and with Israel."

28 So he was there with the LORD forty days and forty nights; he neither ate bread nor drank water. And He wrote on the tablets the words of the covenant, the Ten Commandments.

29 Now it was so, when Moses came down from Mount Sinai (and the two tablets of the Testimony were in Moses' hand when he came down from the mountain), that Moses did not know that the skin of his face shone while he talked with Him.

30 So when Aaron and all the children of Israel saw Moses, behold, the skin of his face shone, and they were afraid to come near him.

31 Then Moses called to them, and Aaron and all the rulers of the congregation returned to him; and Moses talked with them.

32 Afterward all the children of Israel came near, and he gave them as commandments all that the LORD had spoken with him on Mount Sinai.

Word Meaning:
tenor: the meaning of the Lord's words

Questions:

1. What did the Lord tell Moses to do? _____

2. With whom had the Lord made a covenant? _____

3. According to what had he made this covenant? _____
    _____

4. How long was Moses with the Lord? _____

5. What did he not do? _____

6. What did Moses write on the tablets? _____
    _____

7. Describe what Moses looked like when he came down the mountain with the tablets of the Testimony? _____

8. What was the reaction of Aaron and the children of Israel when they saw him?
    _____

9. What did Moses do? _____
    _____

10. What did Moses give them? _____
    _____

4 And Moses spoke to all the congregation of the children of Israel, saying, "This is the thing which the LORD commanded, saying:

5 'Take from among you an offering to the LORD. Whoever is of a willing heart, let him bring it as an offering to the LORD: gold, silver, and bronze.'"

21 Then everyone came whose heart was stirred, and everyone whose spirit was willing, and they brought the LORD's offering for the work of the tabernacle of meeting, for all its service, and for the holy garments.

29 The children of Israel brought a freewill offering to the LORD, all the men and women whose hearts were willing to bring material for all kinds of work which the LORD, by the hand of Moses, had commanded to be done.

33b So Moses finished the work.

34 Then the cloud covered the tabernacle of meeting, and the glory of the LORD filled the tabernacle.

35 And Moses was not able to enter the tabernacle of meeting, because the cloud rested above it, and the glory of the LORD filled the tabernacle.

36 Whenever the cloud was taken up from above the tabernacle, the children of Israel would go **onward** in all their journeys.

37 But if the cloud was not taken up, then they did not journey till the day that it was taken up.

38 For the cloud of the LORD was above the tabernacle by day, and fire was over it by night, in the sight of all the house of Israel, throughout all their journeys.

Word Meaning:
onward: moving forward

Questions:

1. To whom did Moses speak? _____

   _____

2. What did he say the Lord commanded? _____

   _____

3. What did the Lord say about the condition of the giver's heart?_____

   _____

4. What was significant about everyone who came?

   a) _____

   b) _____

5. For what purpose was the offering?

     a) _____

     b) _____

     c) _____

6. What was the offering called? _____

7. Who brought these offerings? _____

_____

8. Who had commanded this work to be done? _____

9. What had Moses accomplished? _____

_____

10. What covered the tabernacle of meeting? _____

11. What filled the tabernacle? _____

12. Why was Moses not able to enter the tabernacle of meeting?

     a) _____

     b) _____

13. What did the children of Israel do whenever the cloud was taken up from above the

tabernacle? _____

14. If the cloud remained above, what did they do? _____

_____

15. What was above the tabernacle by day? _____

16. What was over the tabernacle by night? _____

17. Who could see the cloud and fire? _____

18. How long would it remain? _____

MAP STUDY

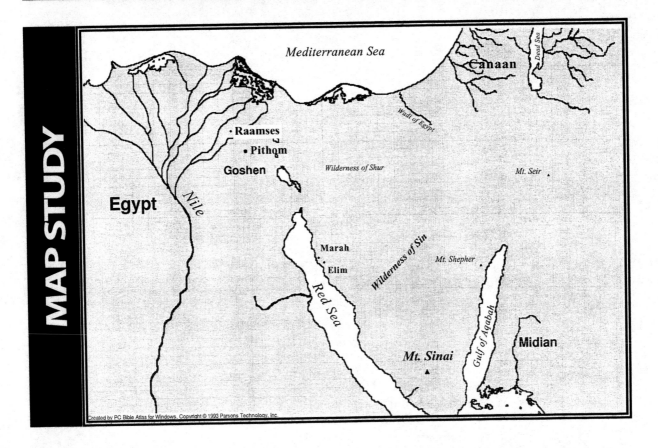

Questions:

1. Draw what you think the tabernacle looked like on your map by Mount Sinai. There is an illustration in many Bibles. [*The Explorer's Bible* published by Thomas Nelson, Inc. (©1991) has an illustration on page 180.]

2. In the space below draw and color

    a) the pillar of cloud (for God's presence during the day).

    b) a pillar of fire (for God's presence during the night).

REVIEW

LESSON
SIXTEEN

Exodus 33 - 40

A. Write the correct letter(s) in the blank.

_____ 1. The Lord promised Moses that
         a) He would give him the best land.
         b) He would give him rest.
         c) His presence would go with him.

_____ 2. In what ways did the Lord say He would show Moses His glory?
         a) He would make His goodness pass before him.
         b) He would proclaim the name of the Lord.
         c) He would be gracious.
         d) He would have compassion.

_____ 3. How did Moses show His respect and awe of the Lord God?
         a) He raised His hands to heaven.
         b) He bowed his head toward the earth.
         c) He worshiped the Lord.
         d) He sang a hymn of praise.

_____ 4. How did God show His presence to the people?
         a) a cloud above the tabernacle by day
         b) a fire over the tabernacle by night
         c) He came to talk to them.
         d) in a bright light

B. Order of events: Put the following in the correct order 1-5.

_____ 1. Moses speaks to the congregation of Israel.

_____ 2. The cloud rested above the tabernacle of meeting.

_____ 3. Moses stood on the rock to see God's glory.

_____ 4. The Lord told Moses to write the words of the covenant on the two new tablets.

_____ 5. The people gave a freewill offering to the Lord.

C. Complete the following from Exodus 40:38.

"For the _____ of the LORD was above the _____ by

_____, and _____ was over it by _____, in the sight of all the house

of Israel, throughout all their _____."

 # DISCOVERY

SIN AND SEPARATION

DAY ONE
LEVITICUS 1:1-3
LEVITICUS 2:1
LEVITICUS 3:1, 17

1 Now the LORD called to Moses, and spoke to him from the tabernacle of meeting, saying,

2 "Speak to the children of Israel, and say to them: 'When any one of you brings an offering to the LORD, you shall bring your offering of the livestock; of the herd and of the flock.

3 'If his offering is a burnt sacrifice of the herd, let him offer a male without **blemish**; he shall offer it of his own **free will** at the door of the tabernacle of meeting before the LORD.

1 'When anyone offers a grain offering to the LORD, his offering shall be of fine flour. And he shall pour oil on it, and put **frankincense** on it.

1 'When his offering is a sacrifice of a peace offering, if he offers it of the herd, whether male or female, he shall offer it without blemish before the LORD.

17 'This shall be a **perpetual** statute throughout your generations in all your dwellings: you shall eat neither fat nor blood.'"

Word Meanings:
1. **blemish:** a flaw or defect
2. **free will:** voluntary, without demanding
3. **frankincense:** a fragrant substance burned as incense
4. **perpetual:** not stopping; lasting a long time
5. **communicated:** to be understood

Questions:

1. From where did the Lord speak to Moses? _____

_____

2. What did He tell Moses to do? _____

3. What did the Lord want **communicated** to them about the offerings they would bring?

_____

_____

4. What should the offering be if it was a burnt sacrifice? _____

_____

5. How should this sacrifice be offered? _____

6.   Where should it be offered? _____

   _____

7.   What was said about the grain offering?

   a) _____

   b) _____

   c) _____

8.   What did the Lord say was important about the peace offering that was a sacrifice from the
   herd? _____

9.   What two things are commanded not to be eaten?

   a) _____

   b) _____

DAY TWO

LEVITICUS 4:1-3,
13-14, 20

1 Now the LORD spoke to Moses, saying,

2 "Speak to the children of Israel, saying: 'If a person sins **unintentionally** against any of the commandments of the LORD in anything which ought not to be done, and does any of them,

3 'if the anointed priest sins, bringing **guilt** on the people, then let him offer to the LORD for his sin which he has sinned a young bull without blemish as a sin offering.

13 'Now if the whole congregation of Israel sins unintentionally, and the thing is hidden from the eyes of the assembly, and they have done something against any of the commandments of the LORD in anything which should not be done, and are guilty;

14 'when the sin which they have committed becomes known, then the assembly shall offer a young bull for the sin, and bring it before the tabernacle of meeting.

20 'And he shall do with the bull as he did with the bull as a sin offering; thus he shall do with it. So the priest shall make **atonement** for them, and it shall be forgiven them.'"

Word Meanings:
1.   **unintentionally:** not done on purpose; accidentally
2.   **guilt:** the fact of being responsible for wrongdoing
3.   **atonement:** payment for sin
4.   **assume:** to take as a fact
5.   **excluded:** to leave out; omit

Questions:

1. To whom did the Lord explain the offering requirement? _____

2. To whom was Moses to speak? _____

3. Give the conditions which require the sacrifice of a young bull without blemish.

   a) _____

   _____

   b) _____

4. What words **assume** that there are no sins that are **excluded**? _____

   _____

5. What is the consequence when an anointed priest sins?_____

   _____

6. Tell what condition is possible in unintentional sin of the whole congregation of Israel?

   _____

7. What is required when the whole congregation of Israel sins unintentionally?_____

   _____

8. When should this be offered for the sin? _____

   _____

9. How will the sins be forgiven them? _____

   _____

DAY THREE

LEVITICUS 4:22-24,
27-28, 31b

22 'When a ruler has sinned, and done something unintentionally against any of the commandments of the LORD his God in anything which should not be done, and is guilty,

23 'or if his sin which he has committed comes to his knowledge, he shall bring as his offering a kid of the goats, a male without blemish.

24 'And he shall lay his hand on the head of the goat, and kill it at the place where they kill the burnt offering before the LORD. It is a sin offering.

27 'If anyone of the common people sins unintentionally by doing something against any of the commandments of the LORD in anything which ought not to be done, and is guilty,

28 'or if his sin which he has committed comes to his knowledge, then he shall bring as his offering a kid of the goats, a female without blemish, for his sin which he has committed.

31b 'So the priest shall make atonement for him, and it shall be forgiven him.'

Questions:

1. Is it considered sin when a ruler does something unintentionally against any of the commandments of the Lord his God? _____

2. What should be offered when the sin which he has committed comes to his knowledge?

   _____

   _____

3. Where will the goat be killed? _____

   _____

4. Why is this necessary? _____

5. What offering must any of the common people bring when they sin?

   a) _____

   b) _____

6. What word means that one might not commit a sin purposely? _____

7. Is there still guilt for doing something against any of the commandments of the Lord?

   _____

8. When should the offering be brought? _____

   _____

9. Who makes atonement for him concerning his sin? _____

10. What will result? _____

1 'If a person sins in hearing the **utterance** of an **oath**, and is a witness, whether he has seen or known of the **matter**; if he does not tell it, he bears guilt.

4 'Or if a person **swears**, speaking thoughtlessly with his lips to do evil or to do good, whatever it is that a man may **pronounce** by an oath, and he is **unaware** of it—when he **realizes** it, then he shall be guilty in any of these matters.

5 'And it shall be, when he is guilty in any of these matters, that he shall **confess** that he has sinned in that thing;

6 'and he shall bring his **trespass** offering to the LORD for his sin which he has committed, a female from the flock, a lamb or a kid of the goats as a sin offering. So the priest shall make atonement for him concerning his sin.

10b 'and it shall be forgiven him.'

17 "If a person sins, and commits any of these things which are forbidden to be done by the commandments of the LORD, though he does not know it, yet he is guilty and shall bear his **iniquity**.

> **18** "And he shall bring to the priest a ram without blemish from the flock, with your **valuation**, as a trespass offering. So the priest shall make atonement for him regarding his **ignorance** in which he **erred** and did not know it, and it shall be forgiven him.
>
> **19** "It is a trespass offering; he has certainly trespassed against the LORD."

Word Meanings:

1. **utterance:** speaking
2. **oath:** a solemn promise or declaration
3. **matter:** something given one's attention
4. **swears:** promises
5. **pronounce:** to speak as a promise
6. **unaware:** not knowing
7. **realizes:** to understand and accept as a fact
8. **confess:** to admit a sin or something done that is wrong
9. **trespass:** offense; a wrong
10. **iniquity:** sin; wickedness
11. **valuation:** determined value of something
12. **ignorance:** state of being unaware
13. **erred:** sinned

Questions:

1. How can a person (a witness) sin in hearing the utterance of an oath?

   _____

2. How is it possible for a person to "swear" ? _____

   _____

3. What should he do when he realizes his sin?

   a) _____

   b) _____

4. What is required for this offering?

   a) _____

   b) _____

5. What happens when this is brought?

   a) _____

   b) _____

6. Is a person guilty when he commits any of the things which are forbidden even though he does not know it? _____

7. What shall he bear?_____

8. What is the required sacrifice? _____

9. What type of offering is this? _____

10. What word is used to show that this sin was done without the person's knowledge?

   _____

1 And the LORD spoke to Moses, saying:

2 "If a person sins and commits a trespass against the LORD by lying to his neighbor about what was delivered to him for safekeeping, or about a **pledge**, or about a robbery, or if he has **extorted** from his neighbor,

3 "or if he has found what was lost and lies concerning it, and swears falsely—in any one of these things that a man may do in which he sins:

4 "then it shall be, because he has sinned and is guilty, that he shall **restore** what he has stolen, or the thing which he has extorted, or what was delivered to him for safekeeping, or the lost thing which he found,

5 "or all that about which he has sworn falsely. He shall restore its full value, add one-fifth more to it, and give it to whomever it belongs, on the day of his trespass offering.

6 "And he shall bring his trespass offering to the LORD, a ram without blemish from the flock, with your valuation, as a trespass offering, to the priest.

7 "So the priest shall make atonement for him before the LORD, and he shall be forgiven for any one of these things that he may have done in which he trespasses."

8 Then the LORD spoke to Moses, saying,

9 "Command Aaron and his sons, saying, 'This is the law of the burnt offering: The burnt offering shall be on the **hearth** upon the altar all night until morning, and the fire of the altar shall be kept burning on it.

13 'A fire shall always be burning on the altar; it shall never go out.

18b 'It shall be a statute forever in your generations concerning the offerings made by fire to the LORD. Everyone who touches them must be holy.'"

3 And Moses said to Aaron, "This is what the LORD spoke, saying: 'By those who come near Me I must be **regarded** as holy; and before all the people I must be glorified.'" So Aaron held his peace.

8 Then the LORD spoke to Aaron, saying:

9 "Do not drink wine or **intoxicating** drink, you, nor your sons with you, when you go into the tabernacle of meeting, lest you die. It shall be a statute forever throughout your generations,

10 "that you may **distinguish** between holy and unholy, and between unclean and clean,

11 "and that you may teach the children of Israel all the statutes which the LORD has spoken to them by the hand of Moses."

Word Meanings:
1. **pledge:** something given as a security deposit or collateral on a loan
2. **extorted:** to get something from someone by force or threats
3. **restore:** to give back in original condition
4. **hearth:** the floor of where the offerings were burned
5. **regarded:** respected; looked upon
6. **intoxicating:** to make drunk
7. **distinguish:** to recognize a difference
8. **consist:** made up of
9. **significance:** importance, meaning, or value

Questions:

1. What sin that a person commits is considered a trespass against the Lord?

    _____

2. Give the circumstances in which this sin is explained.

    a) _____

    _____

    b) _____

    c) _____

    d) _____

    e) _____

    _____

3. What does it say that this person has done and what is the result? _____

    _____

4. What must this person restore?

    a) _____

    b) _____

    c) _____

    _____

    d) _____

    e) _____

    _____

5. In what amount shall he restore it?

    a) _____

    b) _____

6. Then what shall he do? _____

7. When shall he do this? _____

8. To whom shall he bring this offering? _____

9. Of what does this offering **consist**?

      a) _____

      b) _____

10. Who will make atonement for him for forgiveness? _____

11. Where is the burnt offering required to be given? _____

_____

12. How long is it to remain? _____

13. How long must the fire of the altar be burning? _____

14. What would the **significance** of the offerings be? _____

_____

15. Everyone who touches the offerings must be _____.

16. Who did the Lord say must regard Him as holy? _____

_____

17. Before whom must the Lord be glorified? _____

18. What did the Lord command Aaron not to do? _____

_____

19. What were Aaron and his sons to distinguish between?

      a) _____

      b) _____

20. What responsibility did God also give them? _____

_____

MEMORY
PROVERBS 12:17, 19, 22

17 He who speaks truth declares righteousness, but a false witness, deceit.

19 The truthful lip shall be established forever, but a lying tongue is but for a moment.

22 Lying lips are an abomination to the LORD, but those who deal truthfully are His delight.

REVIEW
LESSON SEVENTEEN

Leviticus 1 - 10 (Selected Text)

A. Match the words with their meanings.

_____ 1. unintentionally   a)   voluntary

_____ 2. atonement   b)   sin; wickedness

_____ 3. free will   c)   not done on purpose

_____ 4. iniquity   d)   to give back in original condition

_____ 5. trespass   e)   payment for sin

_____ 6. restore   f)   a wrong; offense

_____ 7. confess   g)   to admit a sin

B. True (T) or False (F): If false, give the correct answer.

_____ 1. It is a more serious sin to steal than to lie.

_____ 2. Joshua was responsible to teach the children of Israel all the statutes which the Lord had spoken.

_____ 3. A person is still guilty of sin even though he does something unintentionally.

_____ 4. When a person realizes his sin, he should confess it.

_____ 5. After a sacrifice has been offered, the person will be forgiven.

C. Bonus!

Who paid the price for our sins so that we no longer have to offer a sacrifice for sin?

_____

DISCOVERY

LESSON 18

HOW SHALL GOD'S PEOPLE LIVE?

DAY ONE
LEVITICUS 16:2, 16, 18a, 20-22

2 and the LORD said to Moses: "Tell Aaron your brother not to come at just any time into the Holy Place inside the veil, before the **mercy seat** which is on the ark, lest he die; for I will appear in the cloud above the mercy seat.

16 "So he shall make **atonement** for the Holy Place, because of the uncleanness of the children of Israel, and because of their **transgressions**, for all their sins; and so he shall do for the tabernacle of meeting which remains among them in the midst of their uncleanness.

18a "And he shall go out to the altar that is before the Lord, and make atonement for it,

20 "And when he has made an end of atoning for the Holy Place, the tabernacle of meeting, and the altar, he shall bring the live goat.

21 "Aaron shall lay both his hands on the head of the live goat, confess over it all the **iniquities** of the children of Israel, and all their transgressions, concerning all their sins, putting them on the head of the goat, and shall send it away into the wilderness by the hand of a **suitable man**.

22 "The goat shall bear on itself all their iniquities to an **uninhabited** land; and he shall release the goat in the wilderness."

Word Meanings:
1. **mercy seat:** the throne of God which was made of gold covering the ark of the covenant
2. **atonement:** the act which brings God and man back together
3. **transgressions:** sins; violations of God's law
4. **iniquities:** sins and wrongs
5. **uninhabited:** a place where no one lives

Phrase Meaning:
suitable man: a man ready and waiting to do the job

Questions:

1. What did the Lord say that Moses must tell Aaron? _____

_____

2. Where was the Holy Place? _____

_____

133

3. What would the Lord do here? _____

_____

4. What would happen if Aaron did not heed the Lord's warning? _____

5. What was Aaron to do for the Holy Place? _____

6. Why must he do this?

    a) _____

    _____

    b) _____

    c) _____

7. To what place should he go? _____

_____

8. What was he to do when he made an end of atoning for the Holy Place, the tabernacle of

meeting, and the altar? _____

9. Then what would Aaron do? _____

_____

10. What would he confess concerning the children of Israel and their sins?

    a) _____

    b) _____

11. Where would Aaron put these? _____

12. What would he do next? _____

DAY TWO
LEVITICUS 18:1-2, 4
LEVITICUS 19:2b,
3-4, 11-18

1 Then the LORD spoke to Moses, saying,

2 "Speak to the children of Israel, and say to them: 'I am the LORD your God.

4 'You shall observe My *judgments* and keep My *ordinances*, to walk in them: I am the LORD your God.

2b 'You shall be *holy*, for I the LORD your God am holy.

3 'Every one of you shall **revere** his mother and his father, and keep My Sabbaths: I am the LORD your God.

4 'Do not turn to idols, nor make for yourselves molded gods: I am the LORD your God.

11 'You shall not steal, nor deal falsely, nor lie to one another.

12 'And you shall not swear by My name falsely, nor shall you **profane** the name of your God: I am the LORD.

13 'You shall not cheat your neighbor, nor rob him. The wages of him who is hired shall not remain with you all night until morning.

14 'You shall not curse the deaf, nor put a **stumbling block** before the blind, but shall fear your God: I am the LORD.

> **15** 'You shall do no **injustice** in judgment. You shall not be **partial** to the poor, nor honor the person of the mighty. In righteousness you shall judge your neighbor.
>
> **16** 'You shall not go about as a **talebearer** among your people; nor shall you take a stand against the life of your neighbor: I am the LORD.
>
> **17** 'You shall not hate your brother in your heart. You shall surely **rebuke** your neighbor, and not bear sin because of him.
>
> **18** 'You shall not take **vengeance**, nor bear any **grudge** against the children of your people, but you shall love your neighbor as yourself: I am the LORD.'"

Word Meanings:

1. **judgments:** decisions made
2. **ordinances:** laws
3. **holy:** an attribute (characteristic) of God; pure and perfect
4. **revere:** honor and respect
5. **profane:** to treat something sacred with irreverence or contempt
6. **stumbling block:** an obstacle (something in the way of); a hindrance to another's progress
7. **injustice:** to violate a person's rights in being unfair
8. **partial:** favoring of one above another
9. **talebearer:** telling stories about others
10. **rebuke:** give criticism (disapproval) to
11. **vengeance:** punishment
12. **grudge:** feeling resentment toward someone
13. **relationships:** the connections between people and how they treat one another

Questions:

1. What did the Lord say when He spoke to Moses? _____

   _____

2. What did the Lord want the people to observe? _____

3. What did He want them to keep? _____

4. Why did the Lord say the people should be holy? _____

   _____

5. How should one consider his mother and his father? _____

6. What other commandments did the Lord remind them of concerning their worship?

   a) _____

   b) _____

   c) _____

7. Give the commands God had given concerning how they should treat one another?

   a) _____

   b) _____

   c) _____

8. How did the Lord explain what behavior toward your neighbors should be?

    a) _____

    b) _____

9. What did the Lord command about the deaf and the blind?

    a) _____

    b) _____

10. What did the Lord say about judging others?

    a) _____

    b) _____

    c) _____

11. What did the Lord say you should tell your brother (neighbor) and do instead of hating him in

    your heart?

    a) _____

    b) _____

    c) _____

12. What final command did the Lord make regarding **relationships** with others? _____

    _____

DAY THREE
LEVITICUS 19:28,
31-32
LEVITICUS 20:6-10,
13, 26

28 'You shall not make any cuttings in your flesh for the dead, nor **tattoo** any marks on you: I am the LORD.

31 'Give no regard to **medium**s and **familiar spirits**; do not seek after them, to be **defiled** by them: I am the LORD your God.

32 'You shall rise before the gray headed and honor the presence of an old man, and fear your God: I am the LORD.

6 'And the person who turns to mediums and familiar spirits, to **prostitute** himself with them, I will set My face against that person and cut him off from his people.

7 'Consecrate yourselves therefore, and be holy, for I am the LORD your God.

8 'And you shall keep My statutes, and perform them: I am the LORD who *sanctifies* you.

9 'For everyone who **curses** his father or his mother shall surely be put to death. He has cursed his father or his mother. His blood shall be upon him.

10 'The man who commits adultery with another man's wife, he who commits adultery with his neighbor's wife, the adulterer and the adulteress, shall surely be put to death.

13 'If a man lies with a male as he lies with a woman, both of them have committed an **abomination**. They shall surely be put to death. Their blood shall be upon them.

26 'And you shall be holy to Me, for I the LORD am holy, and have separated you from the peoples, that you should be Mine.'

Word Meanings:

1. **tattoo:** to make permanent marks on the skin
2. **mediums:** persons through whom spirits of the dead speak
3. **familiar spirits:** demons who come at the call of a medium
4. **defiled:** to be polluted (impure)
5. **prostitute:** to devote to corrupt or unworthy purposes
6. **sancitifies:** set apart for a sacred purpose
7. **curses:** calling down evil or harm on another person
8. **abomination:** an action to be loathed (to feel intense hatred and disgust for)

Questions:

1. What did the Lord command should not be done to the body?

   a) _____

   b) _____

2. What should not be given any regard nor sought after? _____

   _____

3. What will happen if you do? _____

4. Whom should you rise before and honor? _____

5. What is God's second warning of what will happen to those who use mediums and familiar

   spirits?

   a) _____

   b) _____

6. What did the Lord say the people should do?

   a) _____

   b) _____

   _____

7. What does the Lord do for His people? _____

8.   What punishment is there for one who curses his father or his mother?

a) _____

b) _____

9.   What is the punishment for adultery? _____

10. What is an abomination? _____

_____

11. Why did the Lord demand that His people be holy?

a) _____

b) _____

c) _____

DAY FOUR

LEVITICUS
24:15b-22

15b 'Whoever curses his God shall **bear** his sin.

16 'And whoever **blasphemes** the name of the LORD shall surely be put to death. All the congregation shall certainly stone him, the stranger as well as him who is born in the land. When he blasphemes the name of the LORD, he shall be put to death.

17 'Whoever kills any man shall surely be put to death.

18 'Whoever kills an animal shall make it good, animal for animal.

19 'If a man causes **disfigurement** of his neighbor, as he has done, so shall it be done to him—

20 'fracture for fracture, eye for eye, tooth for tooth; as he has caused disfigurement of a man, so shall it be done to him.

21 'And whoever kills an animal shall restore it; but whoever kills a man shall be put to death.

22 'You shall have the same law for the stranger and for one from your own country; for I am the LORD your God.'

Word Meanings:
1. **bear:** be responsible for
2. **blasphemes:** to speak against God
3. **disfigurement:** to spoil the appearance of

Questions:

1.   What is the consequence for one who curses his God? _____

_____

2.   What punishment is given for one who blasphemes the name of the Lord? _____

_____

3. What is the command for those who kill a man? _____

_____

4. What is the law for whoever kills an animal? _____

_____

5. In the circumstance of causing disfigurement, what is the punishment?

a) _____

b) _____

c) _____

6. What law explains all of the above? _____

_____

7. What shall a man do if he kills an animal? _____

8. How is the law different if a man kills another man? _____

9. For whom is the law the same? _____

_____

DAY FIVE
LEVITICUS
25:1-4, 10

1 And the LORD spoke to Moses on Mount Sinai, saying,

2 "Speak to the children of Israel, and say to them: 'When you come into the land which I give you, then the land shall keep a sabbath to the LORD.

3 'Six years you shall **sow** your field, and six years you shall **prune** your vineyard, and gather its fruit;

4 'but in the seventh year there shall be a sabbath of solemn rest for the land, a sabbath to the LORD. You shall neither sow your field nor prune your vineyard.

10 'And you shall consecrate the fiftieth year, and proclaim **liberty** throughout all the land to all its inhabitants. It shall be a **Jubilee** for you; and each of you shall return to his possession, and each of you shall return to his family.'"

Word Meanings:
1. **sow:** plant seeds in the ground
2. **prune:** to trim by cutting away dead branches
3. **liberty:** freedom

4. **Jubilee:** a year of freedom and restoration celebrated every fifty years

Questions:

1. What did the Lord tell Moses on Mount Sinai that he should instruct the people? _____

   _____

2. When would they do this? _____

   _____

3. What could they do for six years?

   a) _____

   b) _____

   c) _____

4. What would happen the seventh year?

   a) _____

   b) _____

5. What would they not do that they had done for six years?

   a) _____

   b) _____

6. What year would be consecrated? _____

7. For what purpose? _____

   _____

8. What was this year to be called? _____

9. What would each one be directed to do?

   a) _____

   b) _____

REVIEW
LESSON
EIGHTEEN

Leviticus 16 - 25 (Selected Text)

A. Write the correct letter(s) in the blank.

_____ 1. Which of these words have a similar meaning?
      a) sin
      b) atonement
      c) iniquities
      d) transgressions
      e) mercy

_____ 2. Which of these commandments did the Lord remind the people of?
      a) Honor your father and your mother.
      b) Keep My Sabbaths.
      c) Do not turn to idols.
      d) You shall not murder.

_____ 3. Which of the following is not a sacrifice for a sin offering?
      a) Passover
      b) the burnt offering
      c) the trespass offering
      d) Jubilee

B. Answer the following.

1. Give the words that summarize all of the commandments regarding relationships with

others: _____

2. What do you think the key word in this book is? _____

3. The title for this lesson is "How Shall God's People Live?" Give your own title to what you

think is important in the book of Leviticus. _____

_____

_____

C. Identify and tell what would happen on these years.

1. the seventh year: _____

_____

2. the fiftieth year: _____

_____

_____

DISCOVERY

IN THE WILDERNESS

DAY ONE
NUMBERS 1:1-15, 19, 46-47, 53b

1 Now the LORD spoke to Moses in the Wilderness of Sinai, in the tabernacle of meeting...saying: **2** "Take a **census** of all the congregation of the children of Israel, by their families, by their father's houses, according to the number of names, every male individually, **3** from twenty years old and above—all who are able to go to war in Israel. You and Aaron shall number them by their armies. **4** And with you there shall be a man from every tribe, each one the head of his father's house. **from 5-15** These are the names of the men who shall stand with you: [a son from each of the following: Reuben, Simeon, Judah, Issachar, Zebulun, Ephraim and Manasseh (Joseph's sons), Benjamin, Dan, Asher, Gad, and Naphtali.]"

19 As the LORD commanded Moses, so he numbered them in the Wilderness of Sinai. **46** All who were numbered were six hundred and three thousand five hundred and fifty. **47** But the Levites were not numbered among them by their fathers' tribe; **53b** the Levites shall keep charge of the tabernacle of the Testimony.

Word Meaning:
1. **census:** an official counting of the people
2. **excluded:** omitted

Questions:

1. Where did the Lord speak to Moses? _____

    _____

2. What did the Lord tell Moses to do? _____

3. How was the congregation of the children of Israel to be numbered?

    a) _____

    b) _____

    c) _____

    d) _____

    e) _____

4. Who would stand with Moses and Aaron when they numbered the armies?

    a) _____

    b) _____

5. How many sons were chosen to be leaders of their fathers' tribes in Israel? _____

6. What did Moses do that the Lord had commanded? _____

_____

7. How many were numbered? _____

_____

8. Which tribe was not numbered by their fathers' tribe? _____

9. For what reason were they **excluded**? _____

_____

DAY TWO
NUMBERS 2:1-2
NUMBERS 6:22-27

1 And the LORD spoke to Moses and Aaron, saying:

2 "Everyone of the children of Israel shall camp by his own **standard**, beside the **emblems** of his father's house; they shall camp some distance from the tabernacle of meeting."

22 And the LORD spoke to Moses, saying:

23 "Speak to Aaron and his sons, saying, 'This is the way you shall bless the children of Israel. Say to them:

24 "The LORD bless you and keep you;

25 "The LORD make His face shine upon you, and be gracious to you;

26 "The LORD lift up His *countenance* upon you, and give you peace."'

27 "So they shall put My name on the children of Israel, and I will bless them."

Word Meanings:
1. **standard:** a distinctive (special) flag posted by each father's house/tent
2. **emblems:** symbols or signs
3. **countenance:** favor or approval

Questions:

1. What did the Lord tell Moses to instruct the children of Israel to do? _____

_____

2. What other explanations of place are given?

    a) _____

    b) _____

3. What did the Lord tell Moses to speak to Aaron about? _____

_____

4. Give five things that are included in this beautiful blessing.

     a) _____

     b) _____

     c) _____

     d) _____

     e) _____

5. What would Aaron and his sons be doing when they said these words? _____

_____

6. What would the Lord do? _____

DAY THREE

NUMBERS 9:15, 17, 18
NUMBERS 10:35-36

15 Now on the day that the tabernacle was raised up, the cloud covered the tabernacle, the tent of the Testimony; from evening until morning it was above the tabernacle like the appearance of fire.

17 Whenever the cloud was taken up from above the tabernacle, after that the children of Israel would journey; and in the place where the cloud settled, there the children of Israel would pitch their tents.

18 At the command of the LORD the children of Israel would journey, and at the command of the LORD they would camp; as long as the cloud stayed above the tabernacle they remained encamped.

35 So it was, whenever the ark set out, that Moses said: "Rise up, O Lord! Let Your enemies be scattered, and let those who hate You flee before You."

36 And when it rested, he said: "Return, O LORD, to the many thousands of Israel."

Questions:

1. What happened on the day that the tabernacle was raised up? _____

_____

2. What other name was given to the tabernacle? _____

3. What was the appearance above the tabernacle from evening until morning? _____

_____

4. What occurred whenever the cloud was taken up from above the tabernacle? _____

_____

5. What did the children of Israel do when the cloud settled? _____

_____

6. At whose command would the children of Israel journey and camp? _____

_____

7. How long would they stay encamped? _____

_____

8. When did Moses say, "Rise up, O Lord!"? _____

_____

9. What did he say about the Lord's enemies? _____

10. What did he say about those who hated the Lord? _____

_____

11. When did he say the words, "Return, O LORD, to the many thousands of Israel"?

_____

DAY FOUR

NUMBERS 11:1-2, 4-6

> **1** Now when the people complained, it displeased the LORD; for the LORD heard it, and His anger was **aroused**. So the fire of the LORD burned among them, and consumed some in the outskirts of the camp.
>
> **2** Then the people cried out to Moses, and when Moses prayed to the LORD, the fire was quenched.
>
> **4** Now the **mixed multitude** who were among them yielded to **intense craving**; so the children of Israel also wept again and said: "Who will give us meat to eat?
>
> **5** "We remember the fish which we ate freely in Egypt, the cucumbers, the melons, the leeks, the onions, and the garlic;
>
> **6** "but now our whole being is dried up; there is nothing at all except this **manna** before our eyes!"

Word Meanings:
1. **aroused:** stirred up
2. **mixed multitude:** people who had come from Egypt with the Israelites
3. **intense:** extreme in degree
4. **craving:** a consuming desire
5. **manna:** the miracle bread that God had sent to the Israelites in the desert

Questions:

1. What displeased the Lord? _____

2. How is the Lord's emotion expressed? _____

3. What happened? _____

4. What resulted from the Lord's displeasure? _____

_____

5. What did the people do? _____

6. What happened when Moses prayed to the Lord? _____

7. What problem did the mixed multitude of people have? _____

_____

8.   How intense was the reaction of the children of Israel? _____

9.   What was their question in the form of a complaint? _____

_____

10. What did they remember that they had eaten freely in Egypt? _____

_____

11. What did they say their condition was now? _____

_____

12. What showed that they were ungrateful for what they did have to eat? _____

_____

<table>
<tr><td>

DAY FIVE

NUMBERS 11:10,
11a, 14, 16a, 17, 31a,
32a, 33

</td><td>

10 Then Moses heard the people weeping throughout their families, everyone at the door of his tent; and the anger of the Lord was greatly aroused; Moses also was displeased.

11a So Moses said to the LORD,

14 "I am not able to bear all these people alone, because the burden is too heavy for me."

16a So the LORD said to Moses, "Gather to Me seventy men of the elders of Israel.

17 "Then I will come down and talk with you there. I will take of the Spirit that is upon you and will put the same upon them; and they shall bear the burden of the people with you that you may not bear it yourself alone."

31a Now a wind went out from the LORD, and it brought quail from the sea and left them fluttering near the camp.

32a And the people stayed up all that day, all night, and all the next day and gathered the quail.

33 But while the meat was still between their teeth, before it was chewed, the wrath of the LORD was aroused against the people, and the LORD struck the people with a very great plague.

</td></tr>
</table>

Questions:

1.   Who else was displeased besides the Lord at the people's attitude? _____

2.   In his frustration, what did Moses tell the Lord that he was unable to bear? _____

_____

3.   Why did he feel he could not do this? _____

_____

4. What did the Lord tell Moses to do? _____

_____

5. What would these chosen men do? _____

_____

6. How did the Lord show concern for Moses? _____

_____

7. What did the Lord do to answer the people's complaining about meat? _____

_____

8. From where did this meat come? _____

9. How did the Lord show his displeasure for the people's complaints?_____

_____

10. Was this the first time that the children of Israel had complained?_____

REVIEW
LESSON
NINETEEN   Numbers 1 - 11 (Selected Text)

A. Write the correct letter(s) in the blank.

_____ 1. The congregation of Israel was to be numbered
a) by families.
b) by their father's houses.
c) according to the number of names.
d) by every male twenty years and older.
e) by all of the above.

_____ 2. What was Moses' instruction for the children of Israel after they had been numbered?
a) They were to have a picnic.
b) They should get ready for worship.
c) They must go directly to the tabernacle.
d) They were to camp by their own standard (flag).

_____ 3. What words did Moses say when the ark of the covenant rested?
a) "Let those who hate You flee before You."
b) "Return, O Lord, to the many thousands of Israel."
c) "Rise up, O Lord!"

_____ 4. What did the people complain about in this lesson?
a) They were hungry.
b) the lack of water
c) the rules God gave
d) There was no meat.

B. Bible Words: Fill in and complete.

"The LORD _____ you and _____ you; the LORD

_____ His face _____ upon you, and be

_____ to you; the LORD _____ up His

_____ upon you, and give you _____."

C. Tell what the above verse means to you and what it says about God's love.

_____

_____

_____

_____

DISCOVERY

SPYING OUT THE LAND

DAY ONE
NUMBERS 13:1-2, 17-21a, 25, 27-28a

1 And the Lord spoke to Moses saying, **2** "Send men to spy out the land of Canaan, which I am giving to the children of Israel; from each tribe of their fathers you shall send a man, every one a leader among them."

17 Then Moses sent them to spy out the land of Canaan, and said to them, "Go up this way into the South, and go up to the mountains, **18** and see what the land is like; whether the people who dwell in it are strong or weak, few or many; **19** whether the land they dwell in is good or bad; whether the cities they inhabit are like camps or strongholds; **20** whether the land is rich or poor; and whether there are forests there or not. Be of good **courage**. And bring some of the fruit of the land." Now the time was the season of the first ripe grapes.

21a So they went up and spied out the land.

25 And they returned from spying out the land after forty days.

27 Then they told [Moses], and said: "We went to the land where you sent us. It truly flows with milk and honey, and this is its fruit.

28a "**Nevertheless** the people who dwell in the land are strong; the cities are **fortified** and very large."

Word Meanings:
1. **courage:** bravery
2. **nevertheless:** even though; in spite of that
3. **fortified:** strong and secure

Questions:

1. What did the Lord instruct Moses to do? _____

   _____

2. Who was giving this land to the children of Israel? _____

3. How would Moses choose whom to send? _____

4. What was the main assignment that Moses gave these men? _____

   _____

5. What details did he give them to report on?

   a) _____

   b) _____

c) _____

d) _____

e) _____

6. What words did he give to encourage them? _____

_____

7. What was his final instruction? _____

_____

8. How long did they stay in the land to spy and get the information Moses had requested?

_____

9. What was the positive part of the report? _____

_____

10. What had they brought to Moses? _____

11. What was the negative report?

a) _____

b) _____

DAY TWO

NUMBERS 13:30-33
NUMBERS 14:1-5

30 Then Caleb quieted the people before Moses, and said, "Let us go up at once and take possession, for we are well able to overcome it."

31 But the men who had gone up with him said, "We are not able to go up against the people, for they are stronger than we."

32 And they gave the children of Israel a bad report of the land which they had spied out, saying, "The land through which we have gone as spies is a land that devours its inhabitants, and all the people whom we saw in it are men of great **stature**.

33 "There we saw the giants...and we were like grasshoppers in our own sight, and so we were in their sight."

1 So all the congregation lifted up their voices and cried, and the people wept that night.

2 And all the children of Israel complained against Moses and Aaron, and the whole congregation said to them, "If only we had died in the land of Egypt! Or if only we had died in this wilderness!

3 "Why has the LORD brought us to this land to fall by the sword, that our wives and children should become victims? Would it not be better for us to return to Egypt?"

4 So they said to one another, "Let us select a leader and return to Egypt."

5 Then Moses and Aaron fell on their faces before all the assembly of the congregation of the children of Israel.

Word Meanings:
1. **stature:** height
2. **contradict:** to say the opposite of
3. **opinion:** a conclusion based on what one personally thinks
4. **majority:** more than half (In this instance, it was ten against going into the land and only two believing that they could.)
5. **exclaim:** to call out, or speak very loudly
6. **imply:** to say something indirectly
7. **specifically:** exactly
8. **insult:** something said that shows great disrespect
9. **proposal:** a suggestion for consideration

Questions:

1. What did Caleb do? _____

   _____

2. How was Caleb's report different from the previous report? _____

   _____

3. What did he say they should do? _____

   _____

4. What reason did he give? _____

   _____

5. How did the other men **contradict** what Caleb said?

   a) _____

   b) _____

6. What else did these men say to cause fear?

   a) _____

   b) _____

   c) _____

7. By whose **opinion** did they think they were like grasshoppers? _____

   _____

8. How did the congregation (children of Israel) react to the report of the **majority**?

   _____

9. Whom did they complain against? _____

10. What two things did they **exclaim**?

    a) _____

    b) _____

11. What did they **imply** with the last exclamation? _____

    _____

12. After they had blamed Moses and Aaron, who else did they blame? _____

13.   What, **specifically**, did they say He had done by bringing them to this land?

     a) _____

     b) _____

14.   What **insult** did they make after all that the Lord had done for them? _____

_____

15.   What was their strong **proposal**? _____

_____

16.   How did Moses and Aaron react in grief? _____

_____

DAY THREE

NUMBERS 14:6-10

> **6** But Joshua the son of Nun and Caleb the son of Jephunneh, who were among those who had spied out the land, tore their clothes;
>
> **7** and they spoke to all the congregation of the children of Israel, saying: "The land we passed through to spy out is an exceedingly good land.
>
> **8 "If the LORD delights in us, then He will bring us into this land and give it to us, 'a land which flows with milk and honey.'**
>
> **9** "Only do not rebel against the LORD, nor fear the people of the land, for they are our bread; their protection has departed from them, and the LORD is with us. Do not fear them."
>
> **10** And all the congregation said to stone them with stones. Now the glory of the LORD appeared in the tabernacle of meeting before all the children of Israel.

Questions:

1.   What did Joshua and Caleb do? _____

2.   What did they say? _____

3.   What did they say would happen if they stayed in the Lord's favor? _____

_____

4.   How did they describe the land to the people again? _____

_____

5.   What did they plead for the people to not do?

     a) _____

     b) _____

6.   What did they say about the people of the land?

     a) _____

     b) _____

7. Whom did Joshua and Caleb say was with them? _____

8. What did they say in conclusion? _____

9. What violent action did the people want to take against Joshua and Caleb? _____

_____

10. Where did the Lord appear? _____

_____

DAY FOUR
NUMBERS 14:11-13a,
19-23, 30

11 Then the LORD said to Moses: "How long will these people reject Me? And how long will they not believe Me, with all the signs which I have performed among them? **12** I will strike them with the pestilence and disinherit them, and I will make of you a nation greater and mightier than they."

13a And Moses said to the LORD: **19** "**Pardon** the iniquity of this people, I pray, according to the greatness of Your mercy, just as You have forgiven this people, from Egypt even until now."

20 Then the LORD said: "I have pardoned, according to your word; **21** but truly, as I live, all the earth shall be filled with the glory of the LORD— **22** because all these men who have seen My glory and the signs which I did in Egypt and in the wilderness, and have put Me to the test now these ten times, and have not heeded My voice, **23** they certainly shall not see the land of which I swore to their fathers, nor shall any of those who rejected Me see it. **30** Except for Caleb the son of Jephunneh and Joshua the son of Nun, you shall by no means enter the land which I swore I would make you dwell in."

Word Meanings:
  1. **pardon:** to forgive

  2. **tolerance:** patience and understanding

Questions:

1. What questions showed that God's **tolerance** for the people's rejection was limited?

    a) _____

    b) _____

2. What had the Lord shown them many times? _____

_____

3. What did He plan for them now?

    a) _____

    b) _____

4. What did the Lord say He would do for Moses who would not be included in this punishment?

_____

5. How did Moses plead for the people? _____

    _____

6. What did Moses say about the character of God? _____

    _____

7. Had the Lord forgiven them before? _____

8. What did the Lord say?

    a) _____

    b) _____

    _____

9. How many times had the people put the Lord to the test? _____

10. What was the sad consequence of the people's rejection? _____

    _____

11. Which two men did the Lord allow to go into the land because they followed Him?

    _____

DAY FIVE

NUMBERS 20:2-3,
7-8, 10-12
NUMBERS 22:1, 3, 4b,
5-6, 20
NUMBERS 23:16,
19-20

2 Now there was no water for the congregation; so they gathered together against Moses and Aaron.

3 And the people **contended** with Moses and spoke, saying: "If only we had died when our brethren died before the LORD!"

7 Then the LORD spoke to Moses, saying,

8 "Take the rod; you and your brother Aaron gather the congregation together. Speak to the rock before their eyes, and it will yield its water; thus you shall bring water for them out of the rock, and give drink to the congregation and their animals."

10 And Moses and Aaron gathered the assembly together before the rock; and he said to them, "Hear now, you **rebels**! Must we bring water for you out of this rock?"

11 Then Moses lifted his hand and struck the rock twice with his rod; and water came out abundantly, and the congregation and their animals drank.

12 Then the LORD spoke to Moses and Aaron, "Because you did not believe Me, to hallow Me in the eyes of the children of Israel, therefore you shall not bring this assembly into the land which I have given them."

1 Then the children of Israel moved, and camped in the plains of Moab on the side of the Jordan across from Jericho.

3 And Moab was exceedingly afraid of the people because they were many, and Moab was sick with dread because of the children of Israel. **4b** Balak the son of Zippor was king of the Moabites at that time.

5 Then he sent messengers to Balaam...saying: **6** "...please come at once, curse this people for me, for they are too mighty for me. Perhaps I shall be able to defeat them and drive them out of the land, for I know that he whom you bless is blessed, and he whom you curse is cursed."

20 And God came to Balaam at night and said to him, "If the men come to call you, rise and go with them; but only the word which I speak to you—that you shall do."

16 Then the LORD met Balaam, and put a word in his mouth, and said, "Go back to Balak, and thus you shall speak."

[Balaam said to Balak:] **19 "God is not a man, that He should lie, nor a son of man, that He should repent. Has He said, and will He not do? Or has He spoken, and will He not make it good?**

20 "Behold, I have received a command to bless; He has blessed, and I cannot **reverse** it."

Word Meanings:

1. **contended:** argued and insisted in a complaining way
2. **rebels:** those who fight against those in authority
3. **reverse:** revoke or annul a decision or decree
4. **deprived:** felt a lack of

Questions:

1. Of what were the people **deprived**? _____

2. Instead of remembering how the Lord had provided for them, what did they do?

   _____

3. What did the Lord tell Moses to do?

   a) _____

   b) _____

   c) _____

4. What would come out of the rock? _____

5. What did Moses do when he gathered the assembly together before the rock?

   _____

6. What were his words to them?

   a) _____

   b) _____

7. Then what did Moses do instead of speaking to the rock as the Lord had commanded?

    _____

8. How did the water come out? _____

9. What did the Lord say as a result of Moses' disobedience to His command?

    _____

    _____

10. Who was the king of Moab? _____

11. Of whom was he afraid? _____

12. Whom did he call for the purpose of cursing the children of Israel? _____

13. What did Balaam tell Balak about God?

    a) _____

    b) _____

    c) _____

    d) _____

14. What did Balaam say that God had commanded him to do? _____

15. What was Balaam unable to do? _____

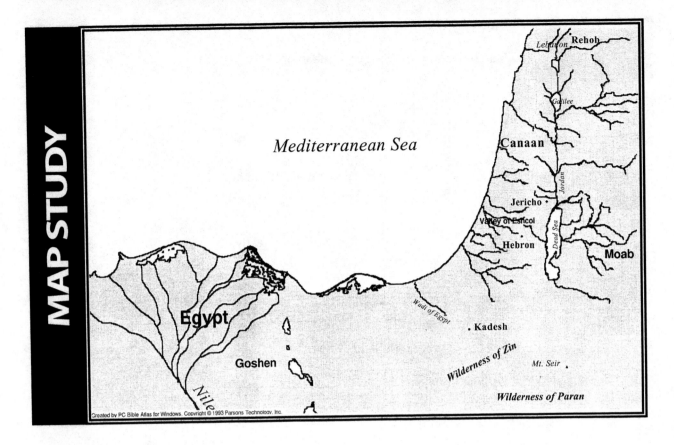

Questions: Read Numbers 12:16-13:3 and 13:17-26.

1. Identify the following: (highlight)

    a) Canaan

    b) The Wilderness of Paran

    c) The Wilderness of Zin

    d) Rehob

    e) Hebron

    f) Valley of Eshcol

    g) Kadesh

2. Trace the spies route to indicate their travel.

3. Identify: Circle these places.

    a) Moab

    b) Jordan

    c) Jericho

REVIEW

LESSON
TWENTY

Numbers 13 - 23 (Selected Text)

A. Match these words with their meaning.

_____ 1. tolerance   a) what one thinks

_____ 2. pardon   b) bravery

_____ 3. imply   c) patience and understanding

_____ 4. opinion   d) to forgive

_____ 5. courage   e) to say something indirectly

B. Complete the following from Numbers 23:19.

"God is not a _____, that He should _____, nor a son of _____,

that He should _____. Has He _____, and will He not _____? Or has

He _____, and will He not make it _____?"

What would be a good paraphrase to say what this verse means?

_____

_____

C. Write the correct letter(s) in the blank.

_____ 1. How often had the people put the Lord to the test?
            a) a few times
            b) many times
            c) exactly ten times
            d) only when they were hungry

_____ 2. How many men had the courage to say they should take the land God had given
            them?
            a) all twelve who went in as spies
            b) two of the men
            c) half of the men

_____ 3. Who were the men who believed God for His promise?
            a) Balak and Balaam
            b) Joshua and Caleb
            c) Moses and Balak

D. Thought Question: Think about how many times you might have tested the Lord. Ask God to
    give you courage to believe and trust Him.

DISCOVERY

LESSON 21

PREPARING TO POSSESS THE LAND

DAY ONE
DEUTERONOMY
1:3, 6-8, 10-11
DEUTERONOMY 2:7
DEUTERONOMY 3:28

3 Now it came to pass in the fortieth year, in the eleventh month, on the first day of the month, that Moses spoke to the children of Israel according to all that the LORD had given him as commandments to them.

6 "The LORD our God spoke to us in Horeb, saying: 'You have dwelt long enough at this mountain. **7** Turn and take your journey... **8** See, I have set the land before you; go in and possess the land which the LORD swore to your fathers—to Abraham, Isaac, and Jacob—to give to them and their descendants after them.'

10 "The LORD your God has multiplied you, and here you are today, as the stars of heaven in multitude. **11** May the LORD God of your fathers make you a thousand times more numerous than you are, and bless you as He has promised you!

7 "For the LORD your God has blessed you in all the work of your hand. He knows your **trudging** through this great wilderness. These forty years the LORD your God has been with you; you have lacked nothing."

[The LORD said to Moses:] **28** "But command Joshua, and encourage him and strengthen him; for he shall go over before this people, and he shall cause them to inherit the land which you will see."

Word Meanings:
1. **trudging:** to walk or march with great effort and difficulty

2. **relating:** communicating

Questions:

1. To whom did Moses speak? _____

2. What was he **relating** to them? _____

    _____

3. What did the Lord tell the people to do?

    a) _____

    b) _____

4. What did Moses say the Lord had done? _____

5. How great were their numbers? _____

6. What blessing did he ask of the Lord for the people? _____

    _____

7. What else had the Lord blessed? _____

8. What did Moses say that the Lord knew? _____

   _____

9. How many years did God provide for them in the wilderness? _____

10. What did the Lord tell Moses to do in regard to Joshua?

    a) _____

    b) _____

    c) _____

11. What would Joshua do that Moses could not do?

    a) _____

    b) _____

DAY TWO

DEUTERONOMY 4:1-2,
6-9, 39
DEUTERONOMY 5:33

1 "Now, O Israel, listen to the **statutes** and the judgments which I teach you to observe, that you may live, and go in and possess the land which the LORD God of your fathers is giving you. **2** You shall not add to the word which I command you, nor take from it; that you may keep the commandments of the LORD your God which I command you.

6 "Therefore be careful to observe them; for this is your wisdom and your understanding in the sight of the peoples who will hear all these statutes, and say, 'Surely this great nation is a wise and understanding people.'

7 "For what great nation is there that has God so near to it, as the LORD our God is to us, for whatever reason we may call upon him? **8** And what great nation is there that has such statutes and righteous judgments as are in all this law which I set before you this day? **9** Only take heed to yourself, and **diligently** keep yourself, lest you forget the things your eyes have seen, and lest they depart from your heart all the days of your life. And teach them to your children and your grandchildren.

39 "Therefore know this day, and **consider** it in your heart, that the LORD Himself is God in heaven above and on the earth beneath; there is no other.

33 "You shall walk in all the ways which the LORD your God has commanded you, that you may live and that it may be well with you, and that you may *prolong* your days in the land which you shall *possess*."

Word Meanings:

1. **statutes:** laws
2. **diligently:** carefully and with serious effort
3. **consider:** to think seriously about
4. **prolong:** to make longer
5. **possess:** to own
6. **unique:** not ordinary; different; exceptional
7. **admonish:** to warn or caution against faults

Questions:

1. Why did Moses tell the people that it was important to listen to the statutes and the judgments?

    a) _____

    b) _____

2. What did he tell them they must not do with these words?

    a) _____

    b) _____

3. Why should they be careful to observe them? _____

    _____

4. What did he remind them of that was **unique** and special for their nation?

    a) _____

    b) _____

    c) _____

5. What did he **admonish** them to do?

    a) _____

    b) _____

6. Why did he caution them so strongly?

    a) _____

    b) _____

7. Besides observing these commandments themselves, what else must they do?

    _____

8. What did Moses want them to know and consider about the Lord?

    a) _____

    b) _____

9. Why did Moses instruct the people to walk in all the Lord's ways?

    a) _____

    b) _____

DAY THREE
DEUTERONOMY
6:4-7, 18
DEUTERONOMY
7:1-4, 6, 9

4 "Hear, O Israel: The LORD our God, the LORD is one! **5 You shall love the LORD your God with all your heart, with all your soul, and with all your strength. 6** And these words which I command you today shall be in your heart. **7** You shall teach them diligently to your children, and shall talk of them when you sit in your house, when you walk by the way, when you lie down, and when you rise up.

18 "And you shall do what is right and good in the sight of the LORD, that it may be well with you, and that you may go in and possess the good land of which the LORD swore to your fathers.

> **1** "When the LORD your God brings you into the land which you go to possess, and has cast out many nations before you... **2** and when the LORD your God delivers them over to you, you shall conquer them and utterly destroy them. You shall make no covenant with them nor show mercy to them. **3** Nor shall you make marriages with them.... **4** For they will turn your sons away from following Me, to serve other gods; so the anger of the LORD will be aroused against you and destroy you suddenly.
>
> **6** "For you are a holy people to the LORD your God; the LORD your God has chosen you to be a people for Himself, a special treasure above all the peoples on the face of the earth. **9** Therefore know that the LORD your God, He is God, the faithful God who keeps covenant and mercy for a thousand generations with those who love Him and keep His commandments."

Questions:

1. What was important for Israel to hear? _____

   _____

2. How shall you love the Lord your God?

   a) _____

   b) _____

   c) _____

3. Where should you keep these words? _____

4. How should these words be taught and to whom should they be taught? _____

   _____

5. When should you talk about these words?

   a) _____

   b) _____

   c) _____

   d) _____

6. When will it be well with you? _____

7. What did the Lord want the people to possess? _____

8. What did the Lord say not to do when they moved into the land regarding the people there?

   a) _____

   b) _____

   c) _____

9. For what reason did God command this? _____

   _____

10. What had the Lord chosen His people to be to Him?

   a) _____

   b) _____

DAY FOUR
DEUTERONOMY
8:2-6, 18
DEUTERONOMY
9:1, 3a, 5

2 "And you shall remember that the LORD your God led you all the way these forty years in the wilderness, to **humble** you and test you, to know what was in your heart, whether you would keep His commandments or not. **3** So He humbled you, allowed you to hunger, and fed you with manna which you did not know...that He might make you know that man shall not live by bread alone; but man lives by every word that proceeds from the mouth of the LORD. **4** Your garments did not wear out on you, nor did your foot swell these forty years. **5** You should know in your heart that as a man **chastens** his son, so the LORD your God chastens you.

6 "Therefore you shall keep the commandments of the LORD your God, to walk in His ways and to fear Him. **18** And you shall remember the LORD your God, for it is He who gives you power to get wealth, that He may establish His covenant which He swore to your fathers, as it is this day.

1 "Hear, O Israel: You are to cross over the Jordan today, and go in to **dispossess** nations greater and mightier than yourself, cities great and fortified up to heaven. **3a** Therefore understand today that the LORD your God is He who goes over before you as a consuming fire.

5 "It is not because of your righteousness or the uprightness of your heart that you go in to possess their land, but because of the wickedness of these nations that the LORD your God drives them out from before you, and that He may fulfill the word which the LORD swore to your fathers, to Abraham, Isaac, and Jacob."

Word Meanings:
1. **humble:** to make not proud
2. **chastens:** disciplines and corrects
3. **dispossess:** take over; conquer

Questions:

1. Who had led these people all the way during forty years in the wilderness?_____

_____

2. What did the Lord say His purpose for them was during this wilderness time?

a) _____

b) _____

c) _____

3. How did the Lord humble His people? _____

_____

4. What did the Lord want them to know from this experience? _____

_____

5. What does man live by? _____

_____

6. What was special about their clothing? _____

_____

7. How does the Lord chasten? _____

8. Who gives the power to get wealth? _____

9. Whom would the children of Israel dispossess? _____

_____

10. Who would go before them as a consuming fire? _____

11. How did the Lord remind the children of Israel that they had not always followed His

commands? _____

_____

12. Why did the Lord say He would drive the nations out? _____

_____

13. Who were their fathers to whom God was keeping His promise? _____

_____

DAY FIVE

DEUTERONOMY
11:7-9, 11-12, 26-28;
12:5, 8; 13:4; 14:29;
15:7-8, 11

7 "but your eyes have seen every great act of the LORD which He did. **8** Therefore you shall keep every commandment which I command you today, that you may be strong, and go in and possess the land which you cross over to possess, **9** and that you may prolong your days in the land which the LORD swore to give your fathers, to them and their descendants, 'a land flowing with milk and honey.' **11** ...a land of hills and valleys, which drinks water from the rain of heaven, **12** a land for which the LORD your God cares; **the eyes of the LORD** your God **are always on it**, from the beginning of the year to the very end of the year.

26 "Behold, I set before you today a blessing and a curse: **27** the blessing, if you obey the commandments of the LORD your God which I command you today; **28** and the curse, if you do not obey the commandments of the LORD your God, but turn aside from the way which I command you today, to go after other gods which you have not known.

5 "But you shall seek the place where the LORD your God chooses, out of all your tribes, to put His name for His dwelling place; and there you shall go. **8** You shall not at all do as we are doing here today—**every man doing whatever is right in his own eyes**. **4** You shall walk after the LORD your God and fear Him, and keep His commandments and obey His voice; you shall serve Him and hold fast to Him.

29 "...the stranger and the fatherless and the widow who are within your gates, may come and eat and be satisfied that the LORD your God may bless you in all the work of your hand which you do.

7 "If there is among you a poor man of your brethren...you shall not harden your heart nor shut your hand from your poor brother, **8** but you shall open your hand wide to him and willingly lend him **sufficient** for his need, whatever he needs. **11** For the poor will never cease from the land; therefore I command you, saying, 'You shall open your hand wide to your brother, to your poor and your needy, in your land.'"

Word Meaning:
    sufficient: enough; an adequate amount

Phrase Meanings:
    1. **the eyes of the LORD are always on it:** God is watching over the land and His people constantly
    2. **every man doing whatever is right in his own eyes:** each person deciding what should be done (not regarding what God has already commanded)

Questions:

1. Describe the land which the Lord wanted His people to possess.

    a) _____

    b) _____

2. How is this land watered? _____

3. How does the Lord feel about this land? _____

4. When are His eyes on it?_____

_____

5. What two things did the Lord set before the people? _____

6. When would each of these occur?

    a) blessing: _____

    b) curse: _____

_____

7. Where should they seek and then go? _____

8. What should they not do? _____

9. Whom should they take care of?

    a) _____

    b) _____

    c) _____

    d) _____

10. How should they care for them? _____

_____

REVIEW
LESSON TWENTY ONE   Deuteronomy 1 - 15 (Selected Text)

A. Write in the answers for each from the list below.

teach	listen	encourage	command	always be with them
widow	stranger	diligently keep	possess the land	remember
strengthen	multiply them	fatherless	consider	

1. List three promises that God gave to the Israelites.

   a) _____

   b) _____

   c) _____

2. List the things God instructed Moses to do with Joshua, the new leader.

   a) _____

   b) _____

   c) _____

3. List five things that God said His people should do regarding His commandments.

   a) _____

   b) _____

   c) _____

   d) _____

   e) _____

4. List whom God's people should take care of.

   a) _____

   b) _____

   c) _____

B. Complete the following from Deuteronomy 5:33.

"You shall walk in all the _____ which the LORD your God has _____

you, that you may _____ and that it may be _____ with you, and that

you may _____ your _____ in the _____ which you

shall _____."

DISCOVERY

KEEPING THE COMMANDMENTS

DAY ONE
DEUTERONOMY
16:19-20;
17:14-15a, 18-19;
18:17-19;
19:15-16, 19-20

[Moses continued to give the commandments of the LORD:] **19** "You shall not **pervert** justice; you shall not show **partiality**, nor take a **bribe**, for a bribe blinds the eyes of the wise and twists the words of the righteous. **20** You shall follow what is altogether just, that you may live and inherit the land which the LORD your God is giving you.

14 "When you come to the land which the LORD your God is giving you, and possess it and dwell in it, and say, 'I will set a king over me like all the nations that are around me,' **15a** you shall surely set a king over you whom the LORD your God chooses; one from among your brethren you shall set as king over you. **18** Also it shall be, when he sits on the throne of his kingdom, that he shall write for himself a copy of this law in a book, from the one before the priests, the Levites. **19** And it shall be with him, and he shall read it all the days of his life, that he may learn to fear the LORD his God and be careful to observe all the words of this law and these statutes."

17 "And the LORD said to me:... **18** 'I will raise up for them a Prophet like you from among their brethren, and will put My words in His mouth, and He shall speak to them all that I command Him. **19** And it shall be that whoever will not hear My words, which He speaks in My name, I will require it of him.'

15 "One witness shall not rise against a man concerning any iniquity or any sin that he commits; by the mouth of two or three witnesses the matter shall be **established**. **16** If a false witness rises against any man to **testify** against him of wrongdoing, **19** then you shall do to him as he thought to have done to his brother; so you shall put away the evil from among you. **20** And those who remain shall hear and fear, and hereafter they shall not again commit such evil among you."

Word Meanings:
1. **pervert:** distort (deceive); use wrongly
2. **partiality:** favoring one over another unfairly
3. **bribe:** to give something in order to receive an undeserving favor; a payoff
4. **established:** proving something to be true
5. **testify:** to state what happened or to give evidence in a court of law

Questions:

1. What three things did the Lord say about justice?

   a) _____

   b) _____

   c) _____

2. What does a bribe do?

      a) _____

      b) _____

3. What did the Lord want them to do? _____

4. When the Lord chooses a king, what shall he do?

      a) _____

      b) _____

5. Why should he do this?

      a) _____

      b) _____

6. What did the Lord tell them about the Prophet He would raise up from among their brethren?

      a) _____

      b) _____

7. What did He say would happen to those who will not hear His words which this prophet speaks?

    _____

8. How should a matter be established concerning any iniquity or sin?_____

    _____

9. What shall you put away ? _____

10. What is the result when this is done?

      a) _____

      b) _____

DAY TWO

DEUTERONOMY
20:1;
21:18-19;
22:5;
23:21, 23;
24:14a, 15;
25:14-15

1 "When you go out to battle against your enemies, and see horses and chariots and people more numerous than you, do not be afraid of them; for the LORD your God is with you, who brought you up from the land of Egypt.

18 "If a man has a **stubborn** and **rebellious** son who will not obey the voice of his father or the voice of his mother, and who, when they have chastened him, will not heed them, 19 then his father and his mother shall take hold of Him and bring him out to the elders of his city, to the gate of his city.

5 "A woman shall not wear anything that **pertains** to a man, nor shall a man put on a woman's **garment**, for all who do so are an **abomination** to the LORD your God.

21 "When you make a vow to the LORD your God, you shall not delay to pay it; for the LORD your God will surely require it of you, and it would be sin to you. 23 That which has gone from your lips you shall keep and perform, for you voluntarily vowed to the LORD your God what you have promised with your mouth.

> **14a** "You shall not **oppress** a hired servant who is poor and needy.
> **15** Each day you shall give him his wages, and not let the sun go down on it, for he is poor and has set his heart on it; lest he cry out against you to the LORD, and it be sin to you.
>
> **14** "You shall not have in your house differing measures, a large and a small. **15** You shall have a perfect and just weight, a perfect and just measure, that your days may be lengthened in the land which the LORD your God is giving you."

Word Meanings:
1. **stubborn:** set on having one's own way
2. **rebellious:** defiant; resisting direction or control; to fight against authority
3. **pertains:** is similar to or belongs to
4. **garment:** an article of clothing
5. **abomination:** something intensely disgusting
6. **oppress:** to rule harshly; to refuse what is owed

Questions:

1. What words are given to encourage one to be courageous when in battle against an enemy?

   a) _____

   b) _____

2. Where should parents take a stubborn and rebellious son? _____

   _____

3. What command is given concerning women's clothing?_____

   _____

4. What command is given for men? _____

5. What should you do when you make a vow to the Lord your God? _____

   _____

6. Why? a) _____

   b) _____

   b) _____

7. When should you give a servant his wages? _____

8. Why? a) _____

   b) _____

   b) _____

9. What kind of measure should one have? _____

   _____

10. What is promised for those who act honestly?_____

   _____

DAY THREE

DEUTERONOMY
26:1-2, 10b-12a,
13, 15, 17-19
DEUTERONOMY
27:2-3a

1 "And it shall be, when you come into the land which the LORD your God is giving you as an inheritance, and you possess it and dwell in it, **2** that you shall take some of the first of all the produce of the ground, which you shall bring from your land that the LORD your God is giving you, and put it in a basket and go to the place where the LORD your God chooses to make His name abide.

10b "Then you shall set it before the LORD your God, and worship before the LORD your God. **11** So you shall rejoice in every good thing which the LORD your God has given to you and your house, you and the Levite and the stranger who is among you.

12a "When you have finished laying aside all the tithe of your increase in the third year—the year of tithing— **13** then you shall say before the LORD your God: 'I have removed the holy tithe from my house, and also have given them to the Levite, the stranger, the fatherless, and the widow, according to all Your commandments which You have commanded me; I have not transgressed Your commandments, nor have I forgotten them. **15** Look down from Your holy **habitation**, from heaven, and bless Your people Israel and the land which You have given us, just as You swore to our fathers, "a land flowing with milk and honey."'"

[Moses said,] **17** "Today you have proclaimed the LORD to be your God, and that you will walk in His ways and keep His statutes, His commandments, and His judgments, and that you will obey His voice. **18** Also today the LORD has proclaimed you to be His special people, just as He promised you, that you should keep all His commandments, **19** and that He will set you high above all nations which He has made, in praise, in name, and in honor, and that you may be a holy people to the LORD your God, just as He has spoken.

2 "And it shall be, on the day when you cross over the Jordan to the land which the LORD your God is giving you, that you shall set up for yourselves large stones, and **whitewash** them with lime. **3a** You shall write on them all the words of this law, when you have crossed over."

Word Meanings:

1. **habitation:** dwelling place
2. **whitewash:** to paint with a mixture used to make white

Questions:

1. What did the Lord say to do when they came into the land?

    a) _____

    b) _____

    _____

2. What shall they do when they set it before the Lord?

    a) _____

    b) _____

3. What commandments did the people follow with the tithe of their increase in the third year?

    a) _____

    b) _____

4. Where is God dwelling? _____

5. What blessing would they ask for?

    a) _____

    b) _____

6. What did Moses say the people had proclaimed?

    a) _____

    b) _____

    c) _____

    d) _____

7. What did the Lord proclaim?

    a) _____

    b) _____

    c) _____

8. What would they do when they crossed over to the land?

    a) _____

    b) _____

DAY FOUR

DEUTERONOMY
28:13, 15, 47-48a,
64-65, 67
DEUTERONOMY
29:9, 13, 29

13 "And the LORD will make you the head and not the tail; you shall be above only, and not be beneath, if you heed the commandments of the LORD your God, which I command you today, and are careful to observe them.

15 "But it shall come to pass, if you do not obey the voice of the LORD your God, to observe carefully all His commandments and His statutes which I command you today, that all these curses will come upon you and overtake you.

47 "Because you did not serve the LORD your God with joy and gladness of heart, for the abundance of everything, **48a** therefore you shall serve your enemies whom the LORD will send against you.

64 "Then the LORD will scatter you among all peoples, from one end of the earth to the other... **65** And among those nations you shall find no rest, nor shall the sole of your foot have a resting place... **67** In the morning you shall say, 'Oh, that it were evening!' And at evening you shall say, 'Oh, that it were morning!' because of the fear which terrifies your heart, and because of the sight which your eyes see.

9 "Therefore keep the words of this covenant, and do them, that you may prosper in all that you do. **13** that He may establish you today as a people for Himself, and that He may be God to you, just as He has spoken to you, and just as He has sworn to your fathers, to Abraham, Isaac, and Jacob. **29** The secret things belong to the LORD our God, but those things which are revealed belong to us and to our children forever, that we may do all the words of this law."

Questions:

1. Would the Lord make the people the head or the tail? _____

2. What was the condition of this blessing? _____

   _____

3. What would happen if they did not follow God? _____

   _____

4. What would result if they did not serve the Lord with joy and gladness?

   a) _____

   b) _____

5. What would the further consequences be?

   a) _____

   b) _____

6. What could they experience if they chose to keep the words of the covenant?

   a) _____

   b) _____

   c) _____

7. To whom do the secret things belong? _____

8. What did God reveal to His people and their children? _____

DAY FIVE

DEUTERONOMY
30:19-20a;
31:6, 14-15, 23, 30;
32:3-4, 45-47;
33:1, 27;
34:5, 7-10

19 "I call heaven and earth as witnesses today against you, that I have set before you life and death, blessing and cursing; therefore choose life, that both you and your descendants may live; **20a** that you may love the LORD your God, that you may obey His voice, and that you may cling to Him, for He is your life and the length of your days.

6 "Be strong and of good courage, do not fear nor be afraid of them; for the LORD your God, He is the One who goes with you. He will not leave you nor *forsake* you."

14 Then the LORD said to Moses, "Behold, the days approach when you must die; call Joshua, and present yourselves in the tabernacle of meeting, that I may **inaugurate** him." So Moses and Joshua went and presented themselves in the tabernacle of meeting. 15 Now the LORD appeared at the tabernacle in a pillar of cloud, and the pillar of cloud stood above the door of the tabernacle. 23 Then He inaugurated Joshua the son of Nun, and said, "Be strong and of good courage; for you shall bring the children of Israel into the land of which I swore to them, and I will be with you."

30 Then Moses spoke in the hearing of all the assembly of Israel the words of this song until they were ended: **3** "For I proclaim the name of the LORD: **Ascribe** greatness to our God. **4** He is the Rock, His work is perfect; for all His ways are justice, a God of truth and without injustice; righteous and upright is He."

45 Moses finished speaking all these words to all Israel, **46** and he said to them: "Set your hearts on all the words which I testify among you today, which you shall command your children to be careful to observe —all the words of this law. **47** For it is not a **futile** thing for you, because it is your life, and by this word you shall prolong your days in the land which you cross over the Jordan to possess."

1 Now this is the blessing with which Moses the man of God blessed the children of Israel before his death. **27** "The eternal God is your **refuge**, and underneath are the everlasting arms; He will thrust out the enemy from before you, and will say, 'Destroy!'"

5 So Moses the servant of the LORD died there in the land of Moab, according to the word of the LORD. **7** Moses was one hundred and twenty years old when he died. His eyes were not dim nor his natural **vigor dimished**. **8** And the children of Israel wept for Moses in the plains of Moab thirty days. So the days of weeping and mourning for Moses ended.

9 Now Joshua the son of Nun was full of the spirit of wisdom, for Moses had laid his hands on him; so the children of Israel heeded him, and did as the LORD had commanded Moses. **10** But since then there has not arisen in Israel a prophet like Moses, whom the LORD knew face to face.

Word Meanings:
1. **forsake:** leave; abandon
2. **inaugurate:** to place into leadership
3. **ascribe:** to assign as an attribute (quality)
4. **futile:** useless; having no effect
5. **refuge:** protection from danger
6. **vigor:** energy; strength (mind and body)
7. **diminished:** decreased or lessened

Questions:

1. What did the children of Israel have to choose between?

   a) _____

   b) _____

2. What did Moses tell them would happen if they chose life?

   a) _____

   b) _____

   c) _____

   d) _____

3. Who is God to this special people?

   a) _____

   b) _____

4. What encouraging words did Moses give the people?

   a) _____

   b) _____

   c) _____

   d) _____

5. Who would lead the children of Israel into the land? _____

6. What did Moses say about God's character when he spoke to the assembly?

   a) _____

   b) _____

   c) _____

   d) _____

   e) _____

   f) _____

7. Why is it not futile for you to observe all the words of this law? _____

   _____

8. Write down the comforting words about God from Moses' last speech.

   a) _____

   b) _____

   c) _____

9. How old was Moses when he died? _____

10. What was his physical condition?

   a) _____

   b) _____

11. How long did the people weep for Moses? _____

12. Why would Joshua be a good leader? _____

13. What were the closing words about Moses?

   a) _____

   b) _____

REVIEW
LESSON
TWENTY TWO

Deuteronomy 16 - 34 (Selected Text)

A. Write the correct letter(s) in the blank.

_____ 1. The Lord said these things about justice.
   a) Do not to show partiality.
   b) Do not to have three witnesses.
   c) Do not pervert justice.
   d) Do not to take a bribe.

_____ 2. The reason the people should not be afraid and have courage is
   a) the land God promised would be given to them without a fight.
   b) the Lord their God was with them.
   c) it is in the law of God.

_____ 3. Which of these were NOT required of the people?
   a) to keep the Lord's commandments
   b) to obey the Lord
   c) to stay close to the Jordan River

_____ 4. What were the blessings of obedience to the Lord?
   a) They would serve their enemies.
   b) They would prosper in all that they did.
   c) The Lord would establish them as His people.

_____ 5. Moses told the people of Israel the Lord said they could choose
   a) life or death.
   b) strength or weakness.
   c) blessing or cursing.

B. Complete the following from Deuteronomy 32:3.

"Ascribe _____ to our God. He is the _____, His work

is _____; for all His ways are _____, a God of _____ and

without _____; righteous and _____ is He."

C. Thinking and Comprehension

"The eternal God is your refuge, and underneath are the everlasting arms" (Deuteronomy 33:27a).

Give a title for this blessing that Moses gave: _____

DISCOVERY

BEING STRONG AND HAVING COURAGE

DAY ONE
JOSHUA 1:1-2,
5b-11, 16

1 After the death of Moses the servant of the LORD, it came to pass that the LORD spoke to Joshua the son of Nun, Moses' assistant, saying: **2** "Moses My servant is dead. Now therefore, arise, go over this Jordan, you and all this people, to the land which I am giving to them—the children of Israel. **5b** As I was with Moses, so I will be with you. I will not leave you nor forsake you. **6** Be strong and of good courage, for to this people you shall divide as an inheritance the land which I swore to their fathers to give them. **7** Only be strong and very courageous, that you may **observe** to do according to all the law which Moses My servant commanded you; do not turn from it to the right hand or to the left, that you may prosper wherever you go. **8** This Book of the Law shall not depart from your mouth, but you shall **meditate** in it day and night, that you may observe to do according to all that is written in it. For then you will make your way **prosperous**, and then you will have good **success**. **9** Have I not commanded you? **Be strong and of good courage; do not be afraid, nor be *dismayed*, for the LORD your God is with you wherever you go."**

10 Then Joshua commanded the officers of the people, saying, **11** "Pass through the camp and command the people, saying, 'Prepare **provisions** for yourselves, for within three days you will cross over this Jordan, to go in to possess the land which the LORD your God is giving you to possess.'" **16** So they answered Joshua, saying, "All that you command us we will do, and wherever you send us we will go."

Word Meanings:
1. **observe:** to abide by; obey
2. **meditate:** study and think about
3. **prosperous:** comfortable; rich in many things (a state of contentment)
4. **success:** a good or favorable outcome
5. **dismayed:** upset and worried
6. **provisions:** all the supplies and things needed for the journey

Questions:

1. Where did the Lord tell Joshua, Israel's new leader, to go? _____

_____

2. What promises did the Lord make to Joshua?

    a) _____

    b) _____

3. Why did the Lord tell him that he needed to be strong and have courage? _____

_____

4. Why did the Lord tell him to be strong and courageous the second time? _____

    _____

5. What did the Lord command that Joshua should not do?

    a) _____

    b) _____

6. What good success would he have if he observed the law? _____

    _____

7. What did the Lord say He had commanded?

    a) _____

    b) _____

8. What would give Joshua confidence for what God commanded? _____

    _____

9. What did Joshua tell the officers to tell the people? _____

10. Where did Joshua say they were going? _____

    _____

11. How many days did they have to get ready? _____

12. How did the people respond to Joshua?

    a) _____

    b) _____

DAY TWO

JOSHUA 2:1, 3-4a,
8-9, 10, 12-14

1 Now Joshua the son of Nun sent out two men from Acacia Grove to spy secretly, saying, "Go, view the land, especially Jericho." So they went, and came to the house of...Rahab, and **lodged** there. **3** So the king of Jericho sent to Rahab, saying, "Bring out the men who have come to you, who have entered your house, for they have come to search out all the country."

4a Then the woman took the two men and hid them. **8** Now before they lay down, she came up to them on the roof, **9** and said to the men: "I know that the LORD has given you the land, that the terror of you has fallen on us, and that all the inhabitants of the land are **fainthearted** because of you.

10 "For we have heard how the LORD dried up the water of the Red Sea for you when you came out of Egypt, and what you did to the two kings of the Amorites who were on the other side of the Jordan, Sihon and Og, whom you utterly destroyed.

12 "Now therefore, I beg you, swear to me by the LORD, since I have shown you kindness, that you also will show kindness to my father's house, and give me a true **token**, **13** ...and deliver our lives from death."

14 So the men answered her, "Our lives for yours, if none of you tell this business of ours. And it shall be, when the LORD has given us the land, that we will **deal** kindly and truly with you."

Word Meanings:
1. **lodged:** to stay for a short time
2. **fainthearted:** lacking in courage
3. **token:** to give evidence (something understood) of an agreement
4. **deal:** an agreement in the way one is to be treated

Questions:

1. Where did Joshua send two men to spy? _____

2. Where did they lodge? _____

3. What did the king of Jericho want Rahab to do? _____

4. Why was he concerned? _____

   _____

5. What did Rahab do with the men? _____

6. What did she say to the men? _____

   _____

7. What did she tell them about the inhabitants of the land?

   a) _____

   b) _____

8. What did she say they had heard?

   a) _____

   b) _____

9. What did she beg the men to do? _____

   _____

10. Why did she think she deserved this? _____

11. What did the men answer her? _____

12. What was their condition for her safety and that of her family? _____

   _____

DAY THREE

JOSHUA 2:15-18, 21-23

15 Then she let them down by a rope through the window, for her house was on the city wall... **16** And she said to them, "Get to the mountain, lest the pursuers meet you. Hide there three days, until the pursuers have returned. Afterward you may go your way."

17 So the men said to her: "We will be blameless of this oath of yours which you have made us swear, **18** unless, when we come into the land, you **bind** this line of **scarlet** cord in the window through which you let us down, and unless you bring...all your father's household to your own home."

> **21** Then she said, "According to your words, so be it." And she sent them away, and they departed. And she bound the scarlet cord in the window.
>
> **22** They departed and went to the mountain, and stayed there three days until the pursuers returned. The pursuers **sought** them all along the way, but did not find them. **23** So the two men returned, descended from the mountain, and crossed over; and they came to Joshua the son of Nun, and told him all that had **befallen** them.

Word Meanings:
1. **bind:** to tie together
2. **scarlet:** a bright red color
3. **sought:** looked for; pursued
4. **befallen:** happened to

Questions:

1. How did Rahab help the men escape from the city? _____

   _____

2. Where was her house? _____

3. What advice did she give them as they left?

   a) _____

   b) _____

   c) _____

4. What did the men tell her to do so that they could keep their promise to her?

   a) _____

   b) _____

5. What did Rahab say? _____

6. Did she put the scarlet cord in the window? _____

7. Where did the men go for three days? _____

8. What did the pursuers do? _____

   _____

9. To whom did the men report when they returned? _____

DAY FOUR

JOSHUA 3:1-3, 5, 14-17

> **1** Then Joshua rose early in the morning; and they set out from Acacia Grove and came to the Jordan, he and all the children of Israel, and lodged there before they crossed over. **2** So it was, after three days, that the officers went through the camp; **3** and they commanded the people, saying, "When you see the ark of the covenant of the LORD your God, and the priests, the Levites, bearing it, then you shall set out from your place and go after it."

> **5** And Joshua said to the people, "Sanctify yourselves, for tomorrow the LORD will do wonders among you."
>
> **14** So it was, when the people set out from their camp to cross over the Jordan, with the priests bearing the ark of the covenant before the people, **15** and as those who bore the ark came to the Jordan, and the feet of the priests who bore the ark dipped in the edge of the water (for the Jordan overflows all its banks during the whole time of harvest), **16** that the waters which came down from upstream stood still, and rose in a heap very far away... **17** Then the priests who bore the ark of the covenant of the LORD stood firm on dry ground in the midst of the Jordan; and all Israel crossed over on dry ground, until all the people had crossed completely over the Jordan.

Questions:

1. When did Joshua rise up? _____

2. To where did he and the children of Israel come? _____

3. What did they do? _____

4. How many days did they stay there? _____

5. What were the people commanded to watch? _____

   _____

6. Who would be bearing this? _____

7. What were their instructions when the ark began moving? _____

8. What did Joshua tell the people to do to get prepared? _____

9. What would the Lord do the next day? _____

10. What happened when those who bore the ark dipped in the edge of the water? _____

    _____

11. What did the people do when the waters were cut off? _____

DAY FIVE
JOSHUA 4:1-11,
13-14, 18

> **1** And it came to pass, when all the people had completely crossed over the Jordan, that the LORD spoke to Joshua, saying: **2** "Take for yourselves twelve men from the people, one man from every tribe, **3** and command them, saying, 'Take for yourselves twelve stones from here, out of the midst of the Jordan, from the place where the priests' feet stood firm. You shall carry them over with you and leave them in the lodging place where you lodge tonight.'"
>
> **4** Then Joshua called the twelve men whom he had appointed from the children of Israel, one man from every tribe; **5** and Joshua said to them: "Cross over before the ark of the LORD your God into the midst of the Jordan, and each one of you take up a stone on his shoulder, according to the number of the tribes of the children of Israel,

6 "that this may be a sign among you when your children ask in time to come, saying, 'What do these stones mean to you?'

7 "Then you shall answer them that the waters of the Jordan were cut off before the ark of the covenant of the LORD; when it crossed over the Jordan, the waters of the Jordan were cut off. And these stones shall be for a memorial to the children of Israel forever."

8 And the children of Israel did so, just as Joshua commanded... 9 Then Joshua set up twelve stones in the midst of the Jordan, in the place where the feet of the priests who bore the ark of the covenant stood; and they are there to this day.

10 So the priests who bore the ark stood in the midst of the Jordan until everything was finished that the LORD had commanded Joshua to speak to the people...and the people hurried and crossed over 11 Then it came to pass, when all the people had completely crossed over, that the ark of the LORD and the priests crossed over in the presence of the people.

13 About forty thousand prepared for war crossed over before the LORD for battle, to the plains of Jericho. 14 On that day the LORD exalted Joshua in the sight of all Israel; and they feared him, as they had feared Moses, all the days of his life.

18 And it came to pass, when the priests who bore the ark of the covenant of the LORD had come from the midst of the Jordan, and the soles of the priests' feet touched the dry land, that the waters of the Jordan returned to their place and overflowed all its banks as before.

Questions:

1. What did the Lord tell Joshua when all the people had completely crossed over the Jordan?

    _____

2. What was Joshua to command? _____

    _____

3. What were the exact instructions about the location?

    a) _____

    b) _____

4. What were the instructions regarding where to take them? _____

    _____

5. To whom would these be a sign? _____

6. What did Joshua say should be told about the meaning of the stones?_____

    _____

7. What did the children of Israel do? _____

8. Where did Joshua set up twelve stones? _____

    _____

9. How long did the priests stay in the midst of the Jordan? _____

_____

10. What happened next? _____

11. Who crossed over when the people were across? _____

_____

12. How many people prepared for war crossed the Jordan that day? _____

13. Whom did the Lord exalt that day? _____

14. What happened when the priests' feet touched dry ground? _____

_____

15. What was the normal condition of the river? _____

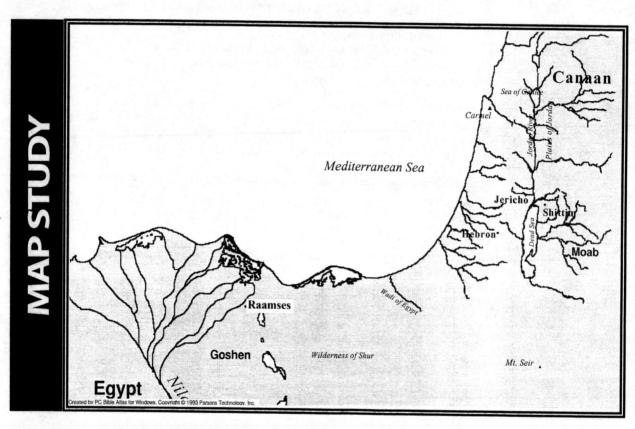

MAP STUDY

1. Use a colored pencil or marker to identify the Jordan River.

2. With a colored pencil or crayon, color the plains of Jordan yellow.

3. Mark the place where the people lodged before they crossed over to the land with an X. (This was across from Jericho.)

4. Mark with a black circle the place where the priests stood until the people had safely crossed the river.

MEMORY
ISAIAH 41:10

> 10 'Fear not, for I am with you; be not dismayed, for I am your God. I will strengthen you, yes, I will help you, I will uphold you with My righteous right hand.'

REVIEW
LESSON
TWENTY THREE

Joshua 1 - 4 (Selected Text)

A. Write a short sentence for each of the **following words**.

1. meditate: _____
   _____

2. prosperous: _____
   _____

3. success: _____
   _____

4. dismayed: _____
   _____

5. bind: _____
   _____

B. True (T) or False (F): If the answer is **false, write** the correct answer below.

_____ 1. The Lord told Moses to **go over** into the land He had promised.

_____ 2. Joshua sent out two **men to spy** and view the land, especially Jericho.

_____ 3. Rahab helped the men **escape the** city by letting them down through a window.

_____ 4. The children of Israel camped for seven days before they crossed the Jordan River.

_____ 5. The priests waited in the midst of the Jordan for the people to cross the river.

C. Write the correct letter(s) in the blank.

_____ 1. Joshua told the officers to tell the people to
      a) build an altar to the Lord.
      b) prepare provisions.
      c) be strong and of good courage.

_____ 2. Rahab told the spies that
      a) she knew that the Lord had given them the land.
      b) her people were ready for battle.
      c) the Israelites could come and live with them in peace.

_____ 3. The Lord told Joshua to
      a) take twelve men, one from every tribe.
      b) take all the children away from the river.
      c) take twelve stones for a memorial.

DISCOVERY

VICTORY AT JERICHO

DAY ONE
JOSHUA 5:1, 10-12

1 So it was, when all the kings of the Amorites who were on the west side of the Jordan, and all the kings of the Canaanites who were by the sea, heard that the LORD had dried up the waters of the Jordan from before the children of Israel until we had crossed over, that **their heart melted**; and **there was no spirit in them** any longer because of the children of Israel.

10 Now the children of Israel camped in Gilgal, and kept the Passover on the fourteenth day of the month at twilight on the plains of Jericho.

11 And they ate of the produce of the land on the day after the Passover, unleavened bread and **parched** grain, on the very same day.

12 Then the manna **ceased** on the day after they had eaten the produce of the land; and the children of Israel no longer had manna, but they ate the food of the land of Canaan that year.

Word Meanings:
1. **parched:** dried

2. **ceased:** stopped

Phrase Meanings:
1. **their heart melted:** they had no courage

2. **there was no spirit in them:** unable to move because of fear

Questions:

1. Which kings were upset by the coming of the children of Israel? _____

2. Where did the Amorites live? _____

3. Where did all the kings of the Canaanites live? _____

4. What had they heard? _____

_____

5. What was possible for the children of Israel when the Lord performed this miracle?

_____

6. What reaction did the kings have? _____

_____

7. Where did the children of Israel camp? _____

8.   What important feast or memorial did they celebrate? _____

9.   At what time of the month was this feast observed? _____

_____

10.   At what time of the day? _____

11.   Where did they celebrate? _____

12.   What did they eat at the Passover feast?

         a) _____

         b) _____

13.   What did they eat on the day after the Passover? _____

_____

14.   What food ceased on the day after they had eaten the produce of the land? _____

DAY TWO
JOSHUA 5:13-15

13 And it came to pass, when Joshua was by Jericho, that he lifted his eyes and looked, and behold, a Man stood opposite him with His sword drawn in His hand. And Joshua went to Him and said to Him, "Are You for us or for our **adversaries**?"

14 So He said, "No, but as Commander of the army of the LORD I have now come." And Joshua fell on his face to the earth and worshiped, and said to Him, "What does my LORD say to His servant?"

15 Then the Commander of the LORD's army said to Joshua, "Take your sandal off your foot, for the place where you stand is holy." And Joshua did so.

Word Meaning:
    adversaries: enemies

Questions:

1.   What did Joshua do when he was by Jericho? _____

2.   What did he see? _____

3.   What did he have in His hand? _____

4.   What questions did Joshua ask when he went near Him? _____

_____

5.   What was the reply? _____

_____

6. What did Joshua do? _____

7. What question did Joshua ask? _____

    _____

8. What did the Commander of the Lord's army say? _____

    _____

9. What did He say about the place where Joshua was standing? _____

10. Did Joshua do as he was commanded?_____

DAY THREE
JOSHUA 6:1-3

> **1** Now Jericho was securely shut up because of the children of Israel; none went out, and none came in.
>
> **2** And the LORD said to Joshua: "See! I have given Jericho into your hand, its king, and the mighty men of **valor**.
>
> **3** "You shall march around the city, all you men of war; you shall go all around the city once. This you shall do six days."

Word Meaning:
  valor: great bravery

Questions:

1. What had happened to Jericho? _____

2. Why? _____

3. What was observed that no one did? _____

    _____

4. What did the Lord want Joshua to see?_____

    _____

5. What did He say of those in Jericho? _____

    _____

6. What were the Lord's instructions? _____

7. For how many days should they do this? _____

DAY FOUR
JOSHUA 6:4-5

> **4** "And seven priests shall bear seven trumpets of rams' horns before the ark. But the seventh day you shall march around the city seven times, and the priests shall blow the trumpets.
>
> **5** "It shall come to pass, when they make a long blast with the ram's horn and when you hear the sound of the trumpet, that all the people shall shout with a great shout; then the wall of the city will fall down flat. And the people shall go up every man straight before him."

Questions:

1.　What would the priests do? _____

2.　What would they be before (in front of)? _____

3.　What would happen the seventh day? _____
_____

4.　What would the priests do on the seventh day? _____

5.　What signal would the people wait for?

　　　a) _____

　　　b) _____

6.　When that happened, what would the people do? _____

7.　What did the Lord say would result? _____

8.　Where should the people go? _____
_____

DAY FIVE
JOSHUA 6:10, 15-17, 23, 25b, 27

> **10** Now Joshua had commanded the people, saying, "You shall not shout or make any noise with your voice, nor shall a word proceed out of your mouth, until the day I say to you, 'Shout!' Then you shall shout."
>
> **15** But it came to pass on the seventh day that they rose early, about the dawning of the day, and marched around the city seven times in the same manner. On that day only they marched around the city seven times. **16** And the seventh time it happened, when the priests blew the trumpets, that Joshua said to the people; "Shout, for the LORD has given you the city!
>
> **17** "Now the city shall be **doomed** by the LORD to destruction, it and all who are in it. Only Rahab...shall live, she and all who are with her in the house, because she hid the messengers that we sent."
>
> **23** And the young men who had been spies went in and brought out Rahab, her father, her mother, her brothers, and all that she had. So they brought out all her relatives and left them outside the camp of Israel. **25b** So [Rahab's descendants dwell] in Israel to this day, because she hid the messengers whom Joshua sent to spy out Jericho.
>
> **27** So the LORD was with Joshua, and his **fame** spread throughout all the country.

Word Meanings:
1. **doomed:** pronounced judgment against   2. **fame:** being well-known

Questions:

1. What important instructions did Joshua give when he spoke to the people? _____

   _____

   _____

2. When could they do differently? _____

3. On which day was the command given? _____

4. What would happen to the city? _____

   _____

5. What was the one exception to all who would perish in the destruction? _____

   _____

6. Why? _____

7. Who went in to rescue Rahab? _____

   _____

8. Who was with Rahab in her house? _____

   _____

9. Where did they take her relatives?_____

10. Who lives in Israel to this day? _____

11. What spread throughout all the country? _____

MAP STUDY

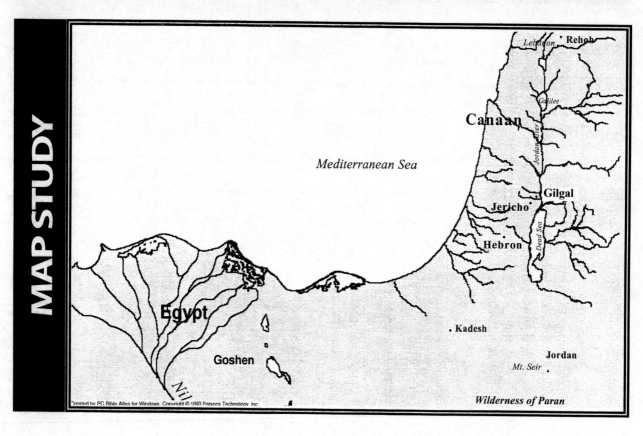

1. Put an X by Gilgal, where the Israelites celebrated the Passover.

2. Draw a wall around Jericho.

3. Color your map (optional).

REVIEW
LESSON
TWENTY FOUR

Joshua 5 - 6 (Selected Text)

A. Write the name of the speaker in the space beside each number.

Commander   the Lord   Joshua

_____ 1. "Are you for us or for our adversaries?"

_____ 2. "Take your sandal off your foot."

_____ 3. "The seventh day you shall march around the city seven times."

B. Give the order in which these events happened.

_____ 1. The Israelites marched around the city.

_____ 2. The Passover was celebrated.

_____ 3. Joshua told the people to shout.

_____ 4. Rahab was rescued by the spies.

_____ 5. A Man with a sword spoke to Joshua.

C. True (T) or False (F): If the answer is false, write the correct answer below.

_____ 1. The Passover was celebrated at noon on the fourteenth day of the month.

_____ 2. All the kings of the Amorites and Canaanites were afraid of the children of Israel.

_____ 3. The Lord instructed the Israelites to march around the city once every day of the week.

_____ 4. The priests with the trumpets went before the ark.

_____ 5. The city was destroyed on the seventh day when the priest blew the trumpets and the people shouted.

_____ 6. Rahab was the only one who was rescued from the destruction of Jericho.

DISCOVERY

SIN IN THE CAMP DELAYS VICTORY

DAY ONE
JOSHUA 7:1-3

1 But the children of Israel committed a trespass regarding the **accursed** things, for Achan...of the tribe of Judah, took of the accursed things; so the anger of the LORD burned against the children of Israel.

2 Now Joshua sent men from Jericho to Ai...and spoke to them, saying, "Go up and spy out the country." So the men went up and spied out Ai.

3 And they returned to Joshua and said to him, "Do not let all the people go up, but let about two or three thousand men go up and attack Ai. Do not **weary** all the people there, for the people of Ai are few."

Word Meanings:
1. **accursed:** under a curse (evil or misfortune pronounced on them)
2. **weary:** to make tired

Questions:

1. What had happened among the children of Israel? _____

   _____

2. What was this regarding? _____

3. Which person was responsible for this trespass? _____

4. Of which tribe was he a member? _____

5. What had Achan done? _____

6. Against whom was the Lord's anger? _____

7. Where did Joshua send men from Jericho? _____

8. What was their purpose? _____

9. What did they tell Joshua on their return?

   a) _____

   b) _____

   c) _____

   d) _____

DAY TWO
JOSHUA 7:4-7

4 So about three thousand men went up there from the people, but they fled before the men of Ai. **5** And the men of Ai struck down about thirty-six men...on the **descent**; therefore **the hearts of the people melted and became like water**.

6 Then Joshua tore his clothes, and fell to the earth on his face before the ark of the LORD until evening, he and the elders of Israel; and **they put dust on their heads**.

7 And Joshua said, "Alas, Lord GOD, why have You brought this people over the Jordan at all—to deliver us into the hand of the Amorites, to destroy us? Oh, that we had been **content**, and dwelt on the other side of the Jordan!"

Word Meanings:
1. **descent:** at the bottom of the hill
2. **content:** satisfied

Phrase Meanings:
1. **the hearts of the people melted and became like water:** the people feared greatly and lost their courage
2. **they put dust on their heads:** a sign of mourning (a time of great sorrow or grief)

Questions:

1. How many men did Joshua send to attack Ai? _____

2. What did these men do? _____

3. How many Israelites were struck down? _____

4. Where were they struck down? _____

5. What happened to the people's hearts because of this defeat? _____

_____

6. What did Joshua do to show his distress? _____

7. What did he do until evening? _____

_____

8. What did Joshua and the elders of Israel do? _____

9. What question did Joshua ask the Lord? _____

_____

10. Who did they think would destroy them? _____

11. What did Joshua wish had been true at that moment? _____

_____

DAY THREE

JOSHUA 7:8-9

[Joshua continued his prayer before the Lord:] **8** "O Lord, what shall I say when Israel turns its back before its enemies?

9 "For the Canaanites and all the inhabitants of the land will hear it, and surround us, and cut off our name from the earth. Then what will You do for Your great name?"

Word Meaning:
  assume: to take for granted; suppose

Questions:

1. What was Joshua's greatest grief expressed to the Lord after their defeat? _____

    _____

2. What did he **assume** would happen when the Canaanites and other inhabitants heard about

    what the children of Israel had done in Ai?

    a) _____

    b) _____

3. What was Joshua's greater concern? _____

    _____

DAY FOUR

JOSHUA 7:10-13a

10 So the LORD said to Joshua: "Get up! Why do you lie thus on your face?

11 "Israel has sinned, and they have also transgressed My covenant which I commanded them. For they have even taken some of the accursed things, and have both stolen and deceived; and they have also put it among their own stuff.

12 "Therefore the children of Israel could not stand before their enemies, but turned their backs before their enemies, because they have become doomed to destruction. Neither will I be with you anymore, unless you destroy the accursed from among you.

13a "Get up, sanctify the people."

Questions:

1. What did the Lord command Joshua to do? _____

2. What question did God ask Joshua? _____

    _____

3. What did the Lord say that Israel had done?

    a) _____

    b) _____

4. How had they sinned against what the Lord had commanded?

    a) _____

    b) _____

5. Because of this sin what had resulted?

    a) _____

    b) _____

    c) _____

6. What was the most terrible outcome of what had happened? _____

_____

7. What could change this condition? _____

_____

8. What command did the Lord give Joshua? _____

DAY FIVE
JOSHUA 7:19-21, 25-26

19 Now Joshua said to Achan, "My son, I beg you, give glory to the LORD God of Israel, and make confession to Him, and tell me now what you have done; do not hide it from me."

20 And Achan answered Joshua and said, "Indeed I have sinned against the LORD God of Israel, and this is what I have done:

21 "When I saw among the **spoils** a beautiful Babylonian garment, two hundred shekels of silver, and a **wedge** of gold weighing fifty shekels, I coveted them and took them. And there they are, hidden in the earth in the midst of my tent, with the silver under it."

25 And Joshua said, "Why have you troubled us? The Lord will trouble you this day." So all Israel stoned him...

26 They raised over him a great heap of stones, still there to this day. So the LORD turned from the fierceness of His anger. Therefore the name of that place has been called the Valley of Achor [Trouble] to this day.

Word Meanings:
1. **spoils:** objects taken as a result of victory in battle

2. **wedge:** a bar

Questions:

1. What three things did Joshua ask Achan, the one who had sinned, to do?

    a) _____

    b) _____

    c) _____

2. What did Achan say? _____

    _____

3. What were the four things that Achan said he did?

    a) _____

    b) _____

    c) _____

    d) _____

4. From your answer above, which of the four were against the Lord's command? _____

    _____

5. What items did Achan covet and take? _____

    _____

6. What did Joshua ask Achan? _____

7. What would happen to Achan as a result of his disgraceful behavior? _____

    _____

8. What was raised over him? _____

    _____

9. What is this place called? _____

MEMORY

EPHESIANS 6:10-11

10 Finally, my brethren, be strong in the Lord and in the power of His might.

11 Put on the whole armor of God, that you may be able to stand against the wiles of the devil.

REVIEW
LESSON
TWENTY FIVE   Joshua 7

A. Write a short summary of what this lesson taught about how serious sin is in the sight of a

   Holy God.

   _____

   _____

   _____

   _____

   _____

   _____

B. Fill in the blanks from the list below.

   sanctify   covenant   destroy   face   Israel

   accursed   coveted   earth   hidden   tore

   1. When the Israelites lost in battle, Joshua

       a)   _____ his clothes

       b)   and fell to the _____.

   2. The Lord commanded Joshua:

       a)   "Get up! Why do you lie thus on your _____.

       b)   _____ has sinned,

       c)   and they have also transgressed My _____ which I commanded
            them."

   3. The Lord instructed Joshua with these words:

       a)   "Neither will I be with you anymore, unless you _____

       b)   the _____ from among you.

       c)   Get up, _____ the people."

   4. Achan confessed his sin and said:

       a)   "I _____ them and took them.

       b)   They are _____ in the earth in the midst of my tent."

DISCOVERY

VICTORY THROUGH OBEDIENCE

DAY ONE
JOSHUA 8:1, 18a, 26

1 Now the LORD said to Joshua: "Do not be afraid, nor be dismayed; take all the people of war with you, and arise, go up to Ai. See, I have given into your hand the king of Ai, his people, his city, and his land."

18a Then the LORD said to Joshua, "Stretch out the spear that is in your hand toward Ai, for I will give it into your hand."

26 For Joshua did not draw back his hand, with which he stretched out the spear, until he had utterly destroyed all the inhabitants of Ai.

Questions:

1. What did the Lord say to Joshua to give him courage? _____

_____

2. What command did the Lord give Joshua? _____

_____

3. What did the Lord say He had given into Joshua's hand?

    a) _____

    b) _____

    c) _____

    d) _____

4. How did the Lord want Joshua to accomplish this victory?_____

_____

5. What did Joshua continue to do until he had destroyed the inhabitants of Ai?_____

_____

DAY TWO

JOSHUA 8:30-32, 34-35

30 Now Joshua built an altar to the LORD God of Israel in Mount Ebal,

31 as Moses the servant of the LORD had commanded the children of Israel, as it is written in the Book of the Law of Moses...And they offered on it burnt offerings to the LORD, and sacrificed peace offerings.

32 And there, in the presence of the children of Israel, he wrote on the stones a copy of the law of Moses, which he had written.

34 And afterward he read all the words of the law, the blessings and the cursings, according to all that is written in the Book of the Law.

35 There was not a word of all that Moses had commanded which Joshua did not read before all the assembly of Israel, with the women, the little ones, and the strangers who were living among them.

Questions:

1. What did Joshua build after this? _____

2. Where did he build this? _____

3. To whom had the Lord given this command? _____

4. For whom was this commandment meant? _____

5. Where is this commandment written? _____

6. What did the people offer on the altar? _____

7. What was sacrificed? _____

8. What did Joshua do in the presence of the children of Israel? _____

   _____

9. What did Joshua read to the people?

   a) _____

   b) _____

10. Who listened to the words Joshua read? _____

11. Which other people are mentioned?

   a) _____

   b) _____

   c) _____

DAY THREE
JOSHUA 9:3-4a, 6, 14-16

3 But when the inhabitants of Gibeon heard what Joshua had done to Jericho and Ai,

4a they worked **craftily**, and went and pretended to be **ambassadors**.

6 And they went to Joshua, to the camp at Gilgal, and said to him and to the men of Israel, "We have come from a far country; now therefore, make a covenant with us."

14 Then the men of Israel took some of their provisions; but they did not ask **counsel** of the LORD.

15 So Joshua made peace with them, and made a covenant with them to let them live; and the rulers of the congregation swore to them.

16 And it happened at the end of three days, after they had made a covenant with them, that they heard that they were their neighbors who dwelt near them.

Word Meanings:
1. **craftily:** clever in a deceitful way
2. **ambassadors:** people sent by a government to represent it in another country
3. **counsel:** advice; instruction

Questions:

1. Which inhabitants heard what Joshua had done to Jericho and Ai? _____

_____

2. What did they do? _____

3. Whom did they pretend to be? _____

4. From where did they tell Joshua they had come? _____

5. What did they want Joshua to make with them? _____

6. What did the men of Israel forget to do? _____

_____

7. What did Joshua do? _____

_____

8. Who else agreed? _____

9. What happened at the end of three days? _____

_____

DAY FOUR
JOSHUA 9:22-26

22 Then Joshua called for them, and he spoke to them, saying, "Why have you deceived us, saying, 'We are very far from you,' when you dwell near us?

23 "Now therefore, you are cursed, and none of you shall be freed from being slaves—woodcutters and water carriers for the house of my God."

24 So they answered Joshua and said, "Because your servants were clearly told that the LORD your God commanded His servant Moses to give you all the land, and to destroy all the inhabitants of the land from before you; therefore we were very much afraid for our lives because of you, and have done this thing.

25 "And now, here we are, in your hands; do with us as it seems good and right to do to us."

26 So he did to them, and delivered them out of the hand of the children of Israel, so that they did not kill them.

Word Meanings:
1. **conclusion:** opinion based on information
2. **submit:** to surrender or yield to the will of another

Questions:

1. What question did Joshua ask the men when he called for them? _____

_____

2. What was the men's punishment as a result? _____

3. What would they always be? _____

4. Which two tasks would they be assigned? _____

_____

5. What did the men have knowledge of that made them fearful for their lives?

   a) _____

   b) _____

6. To what **conclusion** had they come? _____

_____

7. To what were they ready to **submit**? _____

_____

8. What did Joshua do? _____

_____

DAY FIVE

JOSHUA 10:5-6, 8,
12-14

5 Therefore the five kings of the Amorites...gathered together and went up, they and all their armies, and camped before Gibeon and made war against it.

6 And the men of Gibeon sent to Joshua at the camp at Gilgal, saying, "Do not forsake your servants; come up to us quickly, save us and help us, for all the kings of the Amorites who dwell in the mountains have gathered together against us."

8 And the LORD said to Joshua, "Do not fear them, for I have delivered them into your hand; not a man of them shall stand before you."

12 Then Joshua spoke to the LORD...and he said in the sight of Israel: "Sun stand still over Gibeon; and Moon, in the Valley of Aijalon."

13 So the sun stood still, and the moon stopped, till the people had revenge upon their enemies...and did not hasten to go down for about a whole day.

14 And there has been no day like that, before it or after it, that the LORD heeded the voice of a man; for the LORD fought for Israel.

Questions:

1. How many kings of the Amorites gathered together? _____

2. Where did they and their armies go? _____

3. What did the men of Gibeon do? _____

_____

4. What did the Lord tell Joshua? _____

5. Why? _____

6. What would happen? _____

_____

7. Whom did Joshua speak to in the sight of Israel? _____

8. What did he say? _____

9. For how long did it remain that way? _____

10. Had this ever happened before or happened since that time? _____

11. What did the Lord do? _____

12. Who was fighting for Israel? _____

MAP STUDY

Mediterranean Sea

Canaan

Tabor
Galilee
Carmel

Ebal

Plains of Moab

Gibeon. Ai

Jordan

Hebron

Dead Sea

Moab

Wadi of Egypt

Raamses

Pithom

Goshen   Wilderness of Shur   Mt. Seir

Egypt   Nile

Created by PC Bible Atlas for Windows. Copyright © 1993 Parsons Technology. Inc.

1. Draw a circle around Ai.

2. Highlight Mount Ebal, where Joshua built an altar to the Lord.

3. Read Joshua 8:34. Draw two stone tablets by this place. What did Joshua read to the people

    here? _____

4. Locate Gibeon and underline it.

REVIEW
LESSON
TWENTY SIX   Joshua 8 - 10 (Selected Text)

A. Word Meanings: Match the following.

_____ 1. counsel   a) opinion based on information

_____ 2. conclusion   b) clever in a deceitful way

_____ 3. ambassadors   c) advice; instruction

_____ 4. craftily   d) representatives to another country

B. Write the correct letter(s) in the blank.

_____ 1. Which of the following did the Lord say to Joshua?
       a) "Do not be afraid, nor be dismayed."
       b) "None of you shall be freed from being slaves."
       c) "Stretch out the spear that is in your hand."
       d) "Take all the people of war with you, and arise, go up to Ai."

_____ 2. After Joshua built an altar to the Lord, he
       a) wrote on the stones a copy of the law.
       b) went to war with the people of Ai.
       c) read all the words Moses had commanded from the Lord.

_____ 3. The thing that Joshua forgot to do when ambassadors came from another land was
       a) to ask the commanders what they thought.
       b) to ask the counsel of the Lord.
       c) to ask the priests to decide if they were honest.

_____ 4. The ambassadors' punishment for their deceit was
       a) they had to go to war with the Israelites.
       b) they would be woodcutters.
       c) they would be killed.
       d) they would be water carriers.

_____ 5. What miracle did God perform for the Israelites?
       a) The sun stood still.
       b) There was a great thunderstorm.
       c) The enemy was blinded by a great light.
       d) The moon stopped.

_____ 6. For how long did this miracle occur?
       a) from morning until noon
       b) for about two days
       c) for about a whole day

DISCOVERY

POSSESSING THE LAND GOD PROMISED

DAY ONE
JOSHUA 11:15-19, 23
JOSHUA 12:7a, 24b

15 As the LORD had commanded Moses his servant, so Moses commanded Joshua, and so Joshua did. He left nothing undone of all that the LORD had commanded Moses.

16 Thus Joshua took all this land: the mountain country, all the South, all the land of Goshen, the lowland, and the Jordan plain—the mountains of Israel and its lowlands, 17 ...He captured all their kings, and struck them down and killed them. 18 Joshua made war a long time with all those kings.

19 There was not a city that made peace with the children of Israel, except the Hivites, the inhabitants of Gibeon. All the others they took in battle.

23 So Joshua took the whole land, according to all that the LORD had said to Moses; and Joshua gave it as an inheritance to Israel according to their divisions by their tribes. Then the land rested from war.

7a And these are the kings of the country which Joshua and the children of Israel conquered...

24b —all the kings, thirty-one.

Questions:

1. What had Joshua accomplished? _____

   _____

2. What responsibility had he been given? _____

3. Which lands are mentioned?

   a) _____

   b) _____

   c) _____

   d) _____

   e) _____

   f) _____

4. Whom did Joshua capture and kill? _____

5. What did it say took a long time? _____

6. Who made peace from all the lands? _____

7. Of which land were these people the inhabitants? _____

8.   How were the rest of the cities taken who did not make peace? _____

_____

9.   What did Joshua do with the land? _____

_____

10.   How did he do this? _____

11.   How many kings did they conquer? _____

DAY TWO

JOSHUA 13:1b, 6b, 33
JOSHUA 14:1a, 2-3, 5

1b And the LORD said to [Joshua]: "You are old, advanced in years, and there remains very much land yet to be possessed. **6b** I will drive out [the inhabitants] from before the children of Israel; only divide [the land] by lot to Israel as an inheritance, as I have commanded you."

33 but to the tribe of Levi Moses had given no inheritance; the LORD God of Israel was their inheritance, as He had said to them.

1a These are the areas which the children of Israel inherited in the land of Canaan. **2** Their inheritance was by lot, as the LORD had commanded by the hand of Moses, for the nine tribes and the half-tribe. **3** For Moses had given the inheritance of the two tribes and the half-tribe on the other side of the Jordan; but to the Levites he had given no inheritance among them.

5 As the LORD had commanded Moses, so the children of Israel did; and they divided the land.

Questions:

1.   What did the Lord say that Joshua's physical condition was? _____

_____

2.   What did the Lord say that indicated that there was more to accomplish? _____

_____

3.   What did the Lord say He would do before the children of Israel? _____

_____

4.   What responsibility was the Lord giving Joshua? _____

5.   What meaning did the land have to the children of Israel? _____

6.   Which tribe did not receive an inheritance of land? _____

7.   What was their inheritance? _____

8.   How many tribes were given lots in the land of Canaan? _____

9.   Where were the remaining tribes given land? _____

_____

10.   How many tribes received an inheritance of land? _____

DAY THREE
JOSHUA 14:6-7, 9-10

6 Then the children of Judah came to Joshua in Gilgal. And Caleb...said to him: "You know the word which the LORD said to Moses the man of God concerning you and me in Kadesh Barnea.

7 "I was forty years old when Moses the servant of the LORD sent me from Kadesh Barnea to spy out the land, and I brought back word to him as it was in my heart.

9 "So Moses swore on that day, saying, 'Surely the land where your foot has **trodden** shall be your inheritance and your children's forever, because you have wholly followed the LORD my God.'

10 "And now, behold, the LORD has kept me alive, as He said, these forty-five years, ever since the LORD spoke this word to Moses while Israel wandered in the wilderness; and now, here I am this day, eighty-five years old."

Word Meaning:
    trodden: stepped or walked on

Questions:

1. Who came to Joshua with a request? _____

2. From which tribe was he from? _____

3. Of what did he respectfully remind Joshua?_____

   _____

4. How old did Caleb say he was when Moses had sent him to spy out the land?

   _____

5. What report had he brought back to Moses? _____

   _____

6. What did Moses swear to him that day? _____

   _____

   _____

7. Why? _____

8. Whom did Caleb say had kept him alive? _____

9. How long had it been since the Lord spoke this word to Moses in the wilderness?

   _____

10. How old was Caleb now? _____

DAY FOUR
JOSHUA 14:11-14

[Caleb said,] **11** "As yet I am as strong this day as on the day that Moses sent me; just as my strength was then, so now is my strength for war, both for going out and for coming in.

12 "Now therefore, give me this mountain of which the LORD spoke in that day; for you heard in that day how...the cities were great and **fortified**. It may be that the LORD will be with me, and I shall be able to drive them out as the LORD said."

13 And Joshua blessed him, and gave Hebron to Caleb the son of Jephunneh as an inheritance.

14 Hebron therefore became the inheritance of Caleb...because he wholly followed the LORD God of Israel.

Word Meaning:
    fortified: reinforced and strengthened

Questions:

1. What did Caleb say about his strength? _____

   _____

2. For what did he feel he had the strength? _____

   _____

3. What did Caleb ask Joshua to give him for his inheritance? _____

   _____

4. What were the circumstances of the cities in that place? _____

   _____

5. Who did Caleb say may be with him? _____

6. What was the expected result if that were true? _____

   _____

7. What did Joshua do? _____

8. What did Joshua give Caleb as his inheritance? _____

DAY FIVE
JOSHUA 15:13-19

> **13** Now to Caleb...he gave a share among the children of Judah, according to the commandment of the LORD to Joshua namely, Kirjath Arba, which is Hebron (Arba was the father of Anak).
>
> **14** Caleb drove out the three sons of Anak from there... **15** Then he went up from there to the inhabitants of Debir...
>
> **16** And Caleb said, "He who attacks [Debir] and takes it, to him I will give Achsah my daughter as wife." **17** So Othniel...took it; and [Caleb] gave him Achsah his daughter as his wife.
>
> **18** Now it was so, when she came to him, that she persuaded him to ask her father for a field. So she dismounted from her donkey, and Caleb said to her, "What do you wish?"
>
> **19** She answered, "Give me a blessing; since you have given me land in the South, give me also springs of water." So he gave her the upper springs and the lower springs.

Questions:

1. According to whose commandment did Joshua give a share to Caleb?_____

2. What was Caleb's share? _____

3. Whom did Caleb drive out of this land? _____

4. Where did he go from there? _____

5. What arrangement was Caleb willing to make for the one who would attack the inhabitants

    of Debir and succeed in taking it? _____

    _____

6. To whom was Caleb's daughter given? _____

7. What did Caleb's daughter persuade Othniel to do? _____

    _____

8. What did Caleb's daughter do then? _____

    _____

9. What did Caleb ask her? _____

    _____

10. What did his daughter request?_____

11. What did she want the blessing to include? _____

    _____

12. Did Caleb grant his daughter her request? Explain. _____

    _____

MAP STUDY

Map of the region showing the Mediterranean Sea, Canaan, and surrounding locations including Hermon, Valley of Mizpah, Baal Gad, Merom, Hazor, Madon, Galilee, Acshaph, Dor, Shimron, Canaan, Mt. Ebal, Jordan River, Plains of Jordan, Aphek, Gibeon, Ai, Seir, Eglon, Dead Sea, Hebron, Goshen.

Created by PC Bible Atlas for Windows. Copyright © 1993 Parsons Technology, Inc.

1. Color all the land taken by the Israelites with a green colored pencil. (See Joshua 11:16-17.)

2. Circle the land in which the Hivites lived. (See Joshua 11:19.)

3. Read Joshua 13:2-6. Color in the remaining lands from the Jordan to the Great Sea (the Mediterranean Sea) with a purple colored pencil.

MEMORY
COLOSSIANS 3:23-24

23 And whatever you do, do it heartily, as to the Lord and not to men,

24 knowing that from the Lord you will receive the reward of the inheritance; for you serve the Lord Christ.

REVIEW
LESSON
TWENTY SEVEN   Joshua 11 - 15 (Selected Text)

A. Write the correct letter(s) in the blank.

_____ 1. How many tribes received an inheritance of land?
         a) ten tribes
         b) seven tribes
         c) twelve tribes

_____ 2. Which tribe did not receive an inheritance of land?
         a) the tribe of Judah
         b) the tribe of Levi
         c) the tribe of Naphtali

_____ 3. The reason this tribe did not receive land was
         a) because the Lord was their inheritance.
         b) because they had disobeyed the Lord.
         c) because they wanted land that was not available.

_____ 4. Caleb reminded Joshua of a promise that Moses had made to him because he had
         a) given a good report.
         b) wholly followed the Lord.
         c) helped drive the inhabitants out of the land.

B. Match the following people, places, and events.

_____ 1. "I am as strong this day as the day that Moses sent me."

_____ 2. asked for a blessing of springs of water

_____ 3. was old and advanced in years

_____ 4. The land was their inheritance.

_____ 5. "There remains very much land yet to be possessed."

_____ 6. given lots in the land of Canaan

     a) Caleb's daughter   d) Joshua

     b) the Lord   e) Caleb

     c) nine and one-half tribes   f) the children of Israel

DISCOVERY

DIVIDING THE LAND

DAY ONE
JOSHUA 17:14-16a

> **14** Then the children of Joseph spoke to Joshua, saying, "Why have you given us only one lot and one share to inherit, since we are a great people, inasmuch as the LORD has blessed us until now?"
>
> **15** So Joshua answered them, "If you are a great people, then go up to the forest country and clear a place for yourself there in the land of the Perizzites and the giants, since the mountains of Ephraim are too confined for you."
>
> **16a** But the children of Joseph said, "The mountain country is not enough for us; and all the Canaanites who dwell in the land of the valley have chariots of iron."

Questions:

1. To whom did the children of Joseph speak about their dissatisfaction?_____

2. What was their complaint?_____

   _____

3. Why did they think they deserved more? _____

4. What did they emphasize (stress) to Joshua? _____

   _____

5. What words did Joshua repeat with which they had described themselves?_____

   _____

6. What did he tell them to do? _____

   _____

7. Who lived in this land? _____

8. What assumption did Joshua make from their remarks? _____

   _____

9. What further argument did the children of Joseph make? _____

   _____

10. Why did they say they were concerned about taking this land? _____

    _____

DAY TWO
JOSHUA 17:17-18

17 And Joshua spoke to the house of Joseph—to Ephraim and Manasseh—saying, "You are a great people and have great power; you shall not have only one lot,

18 "but the mountain country shall be yours. Although it is wooded, you shall cut it down, and its farthest extent shall be yours; for you shall drive out the Canaanites, though they have iron chariots and are strong."

Questions:

1. What did Joshua say to Ephraim and Manasseh? _____

_____

2. What did he say they shall not have? _____

3. What else would be theirs also? _____

4. What was difficult about this land? _____

5. What did Joshua say they shall do? _____

6. How much of this land would be theirs? _____

7. What else did Joshua say they shall do? _____

8. Did Joshua think that, even though the Canaanites had iron chariots and were strong, they

could take them? _____

DAY THREE
JOSHUA 18:1-4, 9-10

1 Now the whole congregation of the children of Israel assembled together at Shiloh, and set up the tabernacle of meeting there. And the land was **subdued** before them.

2 But there remained among the children of Israel seven tribes which had not yet received their inheritance.

3 Then Joshua said to the children of Israel: "How long will you **neglect** to go and possess the land which the LORD God of your fathers has given you?

4 "Pick out from among you three men for each tribe, and I will send them; they shall rise and go through the land, **survey** it according to their inheritance, and come back to me."

9 So the men went, passed through the land, and wrote the survey in a book in seven parts by cities; and they came to Joshua at the camp in Shiloh.

10 Then Joshua cast lots for them in Shiloh before the LORD, and there Joshua divided the land to the children of Israel according to their divisions.

Word Meanings:
1. **subdued:** conquered
2. **neglect:** to not give proper attention to
3. **survey:** to make and record measurements of the land
4. **reprimand:** a rebuke or scolding

Questions:

1. Where did the congregation of Israel assemble? _____

2. What did they do there? _____

3. What was said about the land? _____

4. How many tribes had not received their inheritance? _____

5. What **reprimand** did Joshua give these tribes? _____

   _____

6. How many men were to be chosen from each tribe? _____

7. What would their assignment be?

   a) _____

   b) _____

   c) _____

8. How did the men complete their survey? _____

   _____

9. What did Joshua do when he received their report? _____

   _____

10. How did Joshua divide the land to the children of Israel? _____

   _____

DAY FOUR

JOSHUA 20:1-6

1 The LORD spoke to Joshua saying, **2** "Speak to the children of Israel saying: '**Appoint** for yourselves **cities of refuge**... **3** that the **slayer** who kills a person accidentally or **unintentionally** may flee there; and they shall be your refuge from the **avenger** of blood.

4 'And when he flees to one of those cities, and stands at the entrance of the gate of the city, and declares his case in the hearing of the elders of that city, they shall take him into the city as one of them, and give him a place, that he may dwell among them.

5 'Then if the avenger of blood pursues him, they shall not deliver the slayer into his hand, because he struck his neighbor unintentionally, but did not hate him beforehand.

6 'And he shall dwell in that city until he stands before the congregation for judgment, and until the death of the one who is high priest in those days. Then the slayer may return and come to his own city and his own house, to the city from which he fled.'"

Word Meanings:
1. **appoint:** choose or select
2. **slayer:** killer
3. **unintentionally:** not done on purpose; not planned

4. **avenger:** a person who wants revenge (to punish someone for harm they might have done)
5. **circumstances:** things that influence someone's actions

Phrase Meaning:
cities of refuge: places to escape to and be safe

Questions:

1. What did the Lord want to remind Joshua to appoint or set aside? _____

   _____

2. What purpose did these cities have? _____

   _____

3. With what **circumstances** would the person be able to go to these cities? _____

   _____

4. Who might pursue him? _____

5. Why may the people in the cities of refuge not deliver the slayer into the hand of the avenger?

   _____

   _____

6. How long shall he remain in the city of refuge?

   a) _____

   _____

   b) _____

   _____

7. What may the slayer do after that time? _____

   _____

DAY FIVE
JOSHUA 21:43-45

43 So the LORD gave to Israel all the land of which He had sworn to give to their fathers, and they took possession of it and dwelt in it.

44 The LORD gave them rest all around, according to all that He had sworn to their fathers. And not a man of all their enemies stood against them; the LORD delivered all their enemies into their hand.

45 *Not a word failed* of any good thing which the LORD had spoken to the house of Israel. All came to pass.

Word Meaning:
    significant: important

Phrase Meaning:
    not a word failed: everything that was promised was given

Questions:

1. What promise had the Lord kept? _____

    _____

2. What two things did the children of Israel do with the land?

    a) _____

    b) _____

3. What else did the Lord provide? _____

4. What happened to all their enemies?

    a) _____

    b) _____

5. What is **significant** about the Lord's words?

    a) _____

    b) _____

REVIEW
LESSON
TWENTY EIGHT

Joshua 17 - 21 (Selected Text)

A. Write the correct letter(s) in the blank.

_____ 1. Who came to Joshua with a request for additional land?
a) the children of Israel
b) the children of Joseph
c) the children of Caleb

_____ 2. When the congregation assembled at Shiloh,
a) they were still at war with their enemies.
b) all of the tribes had received their inheritance.
c) the land was subdued before them.

_____ 3. Joshua divided the land to the children of Israel according to
a) their divisions.
b) first come, first served.
c) the oldest to the youngest.

_____ 4. The assignment Joshua gave to the men chosen from each tribe was to
a) go through the land.
b) survey it according to their inheritance.
c) come back and report to him their findings.

_____ 5. The cities of refuge would be for the purpose of
a) a place to go to if you were angry with someone.
b) a place to go if you had stolen something.
c) a safe place for the one who killed someone accidentally.

B. Who said the following words?

1. "How long will you neglect to go in and possess the land?" _____

2. "Appoint for yourselves cities of refuge." _____

3. "We are a great people."_____

4. "You are a great people and have great power." _____

C. Complete the following from Joshua 21:45.

"Not a word _____ of any _____ thing which the _____ had

_____ to the house of _____. All came to _____."

 # DISCOVERY

REMEMBERING THE COVENANT

1 Now it came to pass, a long time after the LORD had given rest to Israel from all their enemies round about, that Joshua was old, advanced in age.

2 And Joshua called for all Israel, for their elders, for their heads, for their judges, and for their officers, and said to them: "I am old, advanced in age.

3 "You have seen all that the LORD your God has done to all these nations because of you, for the LORD your God is He who has fought for you.

4 "See, I have divided to you by lot these nations that remain, to be an inheritance for your tribes, from the Jordan, with all the nations that I have cut off, as far as the Great Sea westward.

5 "And the LORD your God will **expel** them from before you and drive them out of your sight. So you shall possess their land, as the LORD your God promised you."

Word Meaning:
  expel: to force or drive out

Questions:

1. When did this take place? _____

   _____

2. What is said about Joshua at this time?_____

3. For whom did Joshua call? _____

4. Which four groups did Joshua mention?

   a) _____

   b) _____

   c) _____

   d) _____

5. What did Joshua say they had seen? _____

   _____

6. For whom did the Lord do this?_____

7. How was the Lord involved? _____

8. Why had Joshua divided the nations that remained by lot? _____

_____

9. How far did this land extend? _____

_____

10. What did the Lord want them to do? _____

DAY TWO

JOSHUA 23:6-10

> **6** "Therefore be very courageous to keep and to do all that is written in the Book of the Law of Moses, lest you turn aside from it to the right hand or to the left,
>
> **7** "and lest you go among these nations, these who remain among you. You shall not make mention of the name of their gods, nor cause anyone to swear by them; you shall not serve them nor bow down to them,
>
> **8** "but you shall hold fast to the LORD your God, as you have done to this day.
>
> **9** "For the LORD has driven out from before you great and strong nations; but as for you, no one has been able to stand against you to this day.
>
> **10** "One man of you shall chase a thousand, for the LORD your God is He who fights for you, as He promised you."

Questions:

1. What did Joshua say concerning a desired quality in their character? _____

_____

2. What should they keep and do? _____

_____

3. Why would this be important?

   a) _____

   _____

   b) _____

4. What warning did he give them regarding other nations' gods?

   a) _____

   b) _____

   c) _____

   d) _____

5. What did Joshua say they shall do that they have done to this day? _____

_____

6. What did he say about the nations that had been driven out? _____

_____

7. Had these nations been able to stand against them? _____

8. How did Joshua describe the numbers in terms of fighting men? _____

_____

9. Why were the Israelites so successful? _____

_____

10. What words confirm that God always did what He said He would do? _____

_____

DAY THREE
JOSHUA 23:11-16

> **11** "Therefore take careful heed to yourselves, that you love the LORD your God.
>
> **12** "Or else, if indeed you do go back, and cling to the **remnant** of these nations—these that remain among you—and make marriages with them, and go in to them and they to you,
>
> **13** "know for certain that the LORD your God will no longer drive out these nations from before you. But they shall be **snares** and traps to you, and **scourges** on your sides and thorns in your eyes, until you perish from this good land which the LORD your God has given you.
>
> **14** "Behold, this day I am going the way of all the earth. And you know in all your hearts and in all your souls that not one thing has failed of all the good things which the LORD your God spoke concerning you. All have come to pass for you; not one word of them has failed.
>
> **15** "Therefore it shall come to pass, that as all the good things have come upon you which the LORD your God promised you, so the LORD will bring upon you all harmful things, until He has destroyed you from this good land which the LORD your God has given you.
>
> **16** "When you have transgressed the covenant of the LORD your God, which He commanded you, and have gone and served other gods, and bowed down to them, then the anger of the LORD will burn against you, and you shall perish quickly from the good land which He has given you."

Word Meanings:
1. **remnant:** a part of a group of people that remains
2. **snares:** temptations to sin
3. **scourges:** severe punishment

Questions:

1. What did Joshua plead with the people to do? _____

_____

2. What was the most important thing that would keep them strong? _____

3. Complete Joshua's warning to the children of Israel (Joshua 23:12-13):

    "Or else, if indeed you do go _____, and _____ to the remnant of these

    nations—these that remain among you—and make _____ with them, and go

    in to them and they to you, know for certain that the LORD your God will no longer

    _____ out these nations from before you. But they shall be _____

    and _____ to you, and _____ on your _____ and

    _____ in your _____, until you _____ from this good land

    which the LORD your God has given you."

4. Where did Joshua say he was going? _____

5. What did he remind them of that he had said to them before? _____

    _____

    _____

6. How deeply did they know these things?

    a) _____

    b) _____

7. What words tell that nothing was forgotten or missing? _____

    _____

8. What are the results the children of Israel will receive depending on the choice they make?

    _____

9. How will they continue to know the good things God has promised? _____

    _____

10. When will they know the harmful things? _____

    _____

DAY FOUR

JOSHUA 24:1-4

1 Then Joshua gathered all the tribes of Israel to Shechem and called for the elders of Israel, for their heads, for their judges, and for their officers; and they presented themselves before God.

2 And Joshua said to all the people, "Thus says the LORD God of Israel: 'Your fathers, including Terah, the father of Abraham and the father of Nahor, dwelt on the other side of the River in old times; and they served other gods.

3 'Then I took your father Abraham from the other side of the River, led him throughout all the land of Canaan, and multiplied his descendants and gave him Isaac.

4 'To Isaac I gave Jacob and Esau. To Esau I gave the mountains of Seir to possess, but Jacob and his children went down to Egypt.'"

Questions:

1. To which place did Joshua gather all the tribes of Israel? _____

2. What did the elders, heads, judges and officers do? _____

   _____

3. From what point did the Lord begin His narration of their history? _____

   _____

4. Where did their fathers dwell? _____

5. When did they live there? _____

6. Whom did they serve? _____

7. Tell what the Lord did for Abraham?

   a) _____

   b) _____

   c) _____

   d) _____

8. Whom did the Lord give to Isaac? _____

9. What did He give to Esau? _____

   _____

10. Where did Jacob and his children go? _____

DAY FIVE

JOSHUA 24:5-8

5 'Also I sent Moses and Aaron, and I plagued Egypt, according to what I did among them. Afterward I brought you out.

6 'Then I brought your fathers out of Egypt, and you came to the sea; and the Egyptians pursued your fathers with chariots and horsemen to the Red Sea.

7 'So they cried out to the LORD; and He put darkness between you and the Egyptians, brought the sea upon them, and covered them. And your eyes saw what I did in Egypt. Then you dwelt in the wilderness a long time.

8 'And I brought you into the land of the Amorites, who dwelt on the other side of the Jordan, and they fought with you. But I gave them into your hand, that you might possess their land, and I destroyed them from before you.'

Questions:

1. Whom did the Lord use in Egypt? _____

2. What did He do to Egypt? _____

3. What was the Lord's purpose for this? _____

   _____

4. Where did they come to when the Lord brought them out? _____

5. Who pursued them to the Red Sea? _____

6. How did they pursue them? _____

7. What did the people do when they saw that the Egyptians were pursuing them?

   _____

8. What did the Lord do?

   a) _____

   _____

   b) _____

9. After the people had seen what the Lord did in Egypt, where did they dwell a long time?

   _____

10. To whose land did they come to on the other side of the Jordan? _____

11. What did the Lord do for His people there? _____

    _____

12. Why did the Lord fight for them? _____

    _____

REVIEW
LESSON
TWENTY NINE

Joshua 23:1 - 24:8

A. Write the correct letter(s) in the space given.

_____ 1. Which of these statements is NOT true?
a) The Lord had given the children of Israel rest from their enemies.
b) The land had been divided by lot.
c) The children of Israel had seen all that Joshua had done to the nations.

_____ 2. The reason that the Israelites were so successful was
a) that they were very courageous.
b) that the Lord had fought for Israel.
c) that they had a strong army.
d) that the Israelites were numerous.

_____ 3. The Lord wanted the Israelites to
a) fight their enemies.
b) share their land with foreigners.
c) possess the land.
d) build a temple to the Lord.

_____ 4. Which statement tells the Israelites how they should follow God's laws?
a) by being courageous
b) with understanding and respect for the gods of Egypt
c) without turning aside to the right or to the left

_____ 5. All of these things were to be remembered, but which one was most important?
a) to hold fast to the Lord your God
b) God would always be with them.
c) to take careful heed to yourselves
d) to love the Lord your God

_____ 6. Which of these things did God do for Abraham?
a) He led him throughout the land of Canaan.
b) He parted the Red Sea.
c) He gave him Jacob.
d) He multiplied his descendants.

B. Complete the following from Joshua 23:6.

"Therefore be very _____ to _____ and to _____

all that is written in the Book of the Law of Moses, lest you _____ aside from it to

the _____ hand or to the _____."

 # DISCOVERY

SERVING THE LORD

 **DAY ONE**
JOSHUA 24:9-13

9 'Then Balak the son of Zippor, king of Moab, arose to make war against Israel, and sent and called Balaam the son of Beor to curse you.

10 'But I would not listen to Balaam; therefore he continued to bless you. So I delivered you out of his hand.

11 'Then you went over the Jordan and came to Jericho. And the men of Jericho fought against you—also the Amorites, the Perizzites, the Canaanites, the Hittites, the Girgashites, the Hivites, and the Jebusites. But I delivered them into your hand.

12 'I sent the hornet before you which drove them out from before you, also the two kings of the Amorites, but not with your sword or with your bow.

13 'I have given you a land for which you did not labor, and cities which you did not build, and you dwell in them; you eat of the vineyards and olive groves which you did not plant.'

Questions:

1. What did Balak try to do to the children of Israel? _____

2. Whom did he call to curse Israel? _____

3. Who refused to listen to Balaam? _____

4. What did Balaam continue to do? _____

5. What did the Lord do? _____

6. Where did the people go then? _____
    _____

7. Name the men and nations who fought **against** Israel which the Lord delivered into their hand.

    a) _____   e) _____

    b) _____   f) _____

    c) _____   g) _____

    d) _____   h) _____

8. How did the Lord remind them of how He **went** before them into these lands?
    _____

9. Which kings are mentioned that were **not taken** with Israel's sword or bow?
    _____

10. What privileges did they have as the children of Israel?

a) _____

b) _____

c) _____

_____

DAY TWO

JOSHUA 24:14-18

14 "Now therefore, fear the LORD, serve Him in sincerity and in truth, and put away the gods which your fathers served on the other side of the River and in Egypt. Serve the Lord!

15 "And if it seems evil to you to serve the LORD, choose for yourselves this day whom you will serve, whether the gods which your fathers served that were on the other side of the River, or the gods of the Amorites, in whose land you dwell. But as for me and my house, we will serve the Lord."

16 So the people answered and said: "Far be it from us that we should forsake the LORD to serve other gods;

17 "for the LORD our God is He who brought us and our fathers up out of the land of Egypt, from the house of bondage, who did those great signs in our sight, and preserved us in all the way that we went and among all the people through whom we passed.

18 "And the LORD drove out from before us all the people, including the Amorites who dwelt in the land. We also will serve the LORD, for He is our God."

Word Meanings:
1. **acknowledge:** to confess or admit the truth
2. **affirm:** to express positively

Questions:

1. What should the people do? _____

2. How were they to serve the Lord? _____

3. What should they put away? _____

_____

4. Who was the only one they should serve? _____

5. What if they thought it was evil to serve the Lord? _____

_____

6. When did Joshua say they should decide whom they would serve? _____

7. Whom did Joshua say He would serve?

"But as for me and my house, we will serve the _____."

8.   What words indicate that the people were not tempted to serve other gods? _____

   _____

9.   Whom did they **acknowledge** as the One who brought them out of Egypt? _____

   _____

10. What had they known in Egypt? (How had they been treated?) _____

11. What else did they remember that the Lord had done for them?

   a)   _____

   b)   _____

   c)   _____

12. What did the people **affirm** at the end of their speaking? _____

   _____

DAY THREE

JOSHUA 24:19-21

19 But Joshua said to the people, "You cannot serve the LORD, for He is a holy God. He is a jealous God; He will not forgive your transgressions nor your sins.

20 "If you forsake the LORD and serve foreign gods, then He will turn and do you harm and consume you, after He has done you good."

21 And the people said to Joshua, "No, but we will serve the LORD!"

Word Meaning:
   adequately: appropriately

Questions:

1.   Why did Joshua tell the people that they could not serve the Lord **adequately**?

   a)   _____

   b)   _____

2.   What did he say that the Lord would not forgive?   _____

   _____

3.   When would He not forgive? _____

   _____

4.   What would the consequences be if they did this? _____

   _____

5.   What had the Lord already done? _____

6.   What did the people say to Joshua again? _____

DAY FOUR
JOSHUA 24:22-25

22 So Joshua said to the people, "You are witnesses against yourselves that you have chosen the LORD for yourselves, to serve Him." And they said, "We are witnesses!"

23 "Now therefore," he said, "put away the foreign gods which are among you, and **incline** your heart to the LORD God of Israel."

24 And the people said to Joshua, "The LORD our God we will serve, and His voice we will obey!"

25 So Joshua made a covenant with the people that day, and made for them a statute and an ordinance in Shechem.

Word Meanings:
1. **incline:** to lean toward a certain behavior (put their hearts in the right place)
2. **commitment:** to make a promise that is binding (secure)

Questions:

1. What words did Joshua emphasize to the people so they would understand what a serious matter this choice was? _____

2. What words did the people repeat to confirm their understanding? _____
    _____

3. What did Joshua say they must do to show they meant what they said?
    a) _____
    b) _____

4. What **commitment** did the people make that day?
    a) _____
    b) _____

5. What did Joshua make that day?
    a) _____
    b) _____

6. Where did this take place? _____

DAY FIVE
JOSHUA 24:26-31

26 Then Joshua wrote these words in the Book of the Law of God. And he took a large stone, and set it up there under the oak that was by the sanctuary of the LORD.

27 And Joshua said to all the people, "Behold, this stone shall be a witness to us, for it has heard all the words of the LORD which He spoke to us. It shall therefore be a witness to you, lest you deny your God."

28 So Joshua let the people depart, each to his own inheritance.

29 Now it came to pass after these things that Joshua the son of Nun, the servant of the LORD, died, being one hundred and ten years old.

30 And they buried him within the border of his inheritance at Timnath Serah, which is in the mountains of Ephraim, on the north side of Mount Gaash.

31 Israel served the LORD all the days of Joshua, and all the days of the elders who **outlived** Joshua, who had known all the works of the LORD which He had done for Israel.

Word Meaning:
outlived: lived longer than

Questions:

1. Where did Joshua write all these words? _____

2. What did he do with a large stone? _____

3. Where was this? _____

4. What did Joshua say the significance of this stone was? _____

   _____

5. What would it help them to always remember? _____

   _____

6. What would it help them not to do? _____

7. To where did Joshua let the people depart? _____

   _____

8. What came to pass after these things? _____

   _____

9. How old was he? _____

10. Where did the people bury him? _____

    _____

11. When did the people serve the Lord?

    a) _____

    b) _____

12. What had all these people known? _____

    _____

REVIEW
LESSON THIRTY   Joshua 24:9-31

A. Complete the following from Joshua 24:15.

"_____ for yourselves this _____ whom you will _____...

But as for me and my _____, we will serve the _____."

B. Thought Questions

1. Name at least four important things you have learned from this study about the character
   of God. _____

   _____

   _____

   _____

   _____

   _____

   _____

2. Briefly tell what you have learned that will encourage you to take seriously God's plan and
   purpose for YOU. _____

   _____

   _____

   _____

   _____

3. Accepting God's love and following Him is the most important decision you will ever make.

   a) Is it possible to obey God's commandments all by yourself? _____

   b) Whom did God send in the New Testament to be our sacrifice so that we could
       live right before God? (See John 3:16-17.) _____

4. What will you do if you have now made a commitment to the Lord to continue to know
   how He wants you to live?

   pray _____   study the Bible _____

   be with others who love Him _____   worship Him _____

REMEMBER...YOU can KNOW that He will ALWAYS be with YOU!